M000219365

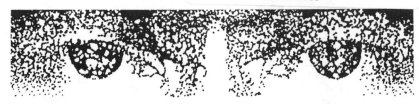

DEFENSIVE LIVING

When Defensive Driving, Diets and Exercise Aren't Enough to Keep You Alive and Well!

BO HARDY

With a Foreword by
Richard D. Smith

DEFENSIVE LIVING™ PRESS

DEFENSIVE LIVING™ PRESS
904 Deer Run S
Pine Bluff, AR 71603

ISBN 0-9633237-9-2

Printed in the United States of America
First Printing: June 1992
Second Printing: March 1993
Third Printing: December 1993
Fourth/Revised Printing: January 1995

Library of Congress Card Catalogue Number
92-90632

DEFENSIVE LIVING

When Defensive Driving, Diets and Exercise Aren't Enough to Keep You Alive and Well!

BO HARDY

Foreword

As I walked onto the parking lot alone, heading for home, I saw the large, rough-looking thugs sitting on my car.

I had studied martial arts for over fourteen years and was ready and willing to do battle if necessary. However, I wasn't in a hurry, so I decided I was now mature enough and smart enough not to push my luck, and I turned around and went back inside. I knew the three thugs would leave eventually and I would go home without a confrontation.

An hour later I again headed for home. It was dark as I walked onto the lot and mine was the only car left, and sure enough, no thugs. As I approached my car, I realized all of the windows were smashed and all four tires were flat.

OUTTHINKING AN ASSAILANT

I grew up in a town of about fifty thousand people, Pine Bluff, Arkansas. My father and I talked many times about what profession I wanted to enter and I had decided I wanted to become an Architect.

For my first summer high school job, I went to a construction site near where we lived and asked to see the boss. I couldn't believe it when he said I could start the next day.

Two years later, my first employer, Cliff Putman, became my karate teacher and immediately introduced me to his teacher, Bo Hardy. Six months later, my class was advanced into one of Mr. Hardy's classes.

I have been training under him ever since and have thrown hundreds of thousands of blocks, punches and kicks and lost hundreds of gallons of perspiration and a pint or two of blood.

Fourteen years after starting martial arts, I was walking alone on a parking lot faced with three thugs sitting on my car. At the time, I was taking my 2nd Degree black belt test and Sensei (Teacher) Hardy had just described the situation above and was asking me what I would do.

I thought I had given an intelligent solution by saying I would just walk away, rather than fight. He then asked me what I would do if I came back out and found my car windows smashed and the tires slashed. Would it bother me, as a Black Belt, to have done nothing to prevent it? I didn't answer, but I knew it would. Sensei Hardy was preparing me for DEFENSIVE LIVING.

TEN TIPS

When Sensei Hardy first asked me to assist him with an assault prevention book, I assumed it was to be a book on punching and kicking. He, however, described it as a book on how to "fight smarter, not harder," about learning to outthink a potential assailant.

He began teaching me alternatives to either becoming a victim or physically fighting back. Those alternatives are in this book!

Once you have read *DEFENSIVE LIVING, When Defensive Driving, Diets and Exercise Aren't Enough To Keep You Alive and Well!*, study the Ten Tips and begin to put them into your daily life. You don't have to do it all at once. Just take one item that makes sense to you and begin to apply it daily, eventually making it a habit. Then take a second item, then a third and so on until you are finally truly practicing DEFENSIVE LIVING. You will greatly reduce your chances of becoming a victim. I know I have. And share these concepts with your family and friends, if you care for their well-being.

Great for gifts!

Just give us your list and $2.00 postage and handling each and we'll send them direct, in your name.

- Birthdays
- Employee Gifts
- Christmas
- Graduation

Discounts

Buying 10 or more copies?
Inquire about quantity discounts.

- Safety Programs
- Sales Promotions
- Employee Programs
- Fund Raising
- Crime Watch Programs

ORDER FORM

DEFENSIVE LIVING™ PRESS
904 Deer Run S.
Pine Bluff, AR 71603

Please send me:

Amount

_____ copies of *DEFENSIVE LIVING: When Defensive Driving, Diets and Exercise Aren't Enough to Keep You Alive and Well!* @ $12.95 each   _____

Arkansas residents please add $0.71 sales tax per book   _____

Postage and Handling @ $2.00 per book   _____

Total $_____

I am paying by: check ____ Visa - MasterCard # _____

Expiration Date _____

Signature _____

OR JUST CALL
1-800-467-1900

LIVING PROGRAMS

Pepper Spray (OC) Personal Protection Weapons Systems

Are you looking for an effective and easy to use personal protection weapon? OC is an organically based, less than lethal spray. Unlike tear gas, it will effectively subdue all types of human and animal subjects who are not responsive to pain, including those who are under the influence of drugs, alcohol and those who are mentally unbalanced. Its effect is instantaneous, resulting in immediate blindness, coughing, and choking. It has ben approved by the F.B.I. for use by its Special Agents. It is effective and requires no physical contact with an assailant. Learn to properly use the most effective personal protection weapon available. Our instructors are certified by two of the largest producers of OC products.

Separate OC Courses are Available for Law Enforcement and Civilian Certification

Taiho-Ryu Karate & Jiu-Jitsu

A martial arts system that stresses realistic, practical self-defense for men, women, children and law enforcement officers. This is not sport karate. Taiho-Ryu is an American system, originally derived from the system used by the Japanese police. You will receive training in awareness, avoidance and passive resistance, as well as effective physical counter action and weapon defense.

Schools are located in:
Pine Bluff, Dumas, Little Rock, Monticello, Star City, Sheridan, and Stuttgart, Arkansas and Dallas/Ft. Worth, Texas.

DEFENSIVE LIVING™
Ten Tips for Assault and Rape Prevention

Tip 1 — Don't Think and Look Like a Victim.

Tip 2 — Always Lock the Doors In Your Car and Home Immediately After Entering or Exiting.

Tip 3 — Always Use the Buddy System.

Tip 4 — Take 15 to 30 Seconds to Observe Your Destination Area Before Approaching.

Tip 5 — If You Decide to Physically Resist Your Assailant, Do So Only to Avoid Personal Injury or Death.

Tip 6 — If You Are Going to Carry a Weapon, Know How to Use It and Have It Available.

Tip 7 — Determine Safe Locations Available 24 Hours a Day In Your City and On Frequently Traveled Routes.

Tip 8 — Become Aware of Crime Trends and Criminal Characteristics.

Tip 9 — When Confronted With Abduction, Never Leave a Public Area, Even when Threatened with Death or Injury.

Tip 10 — Use Positive Mental Survival Training.

From the book, *DEFENSIVE LIVING, When Defensive Driving, Diets and Exercise Aren't Enough to Keep You Alive and Well!* by Bo Hardy — Copyright © 1992

1-800-467-1900

DEFENSIVE

CONVENTIONS
- Keynote Address
- Breakout Sessions
- Spouse Programs

EDUCATION
- Administration
- Teacher Workshops
- Student Programs

BUSINESS
- Corporate Retreats
- Sales Meetings
- Safety Programs
- Wellness Programs

LAW ENFORCEMENT
- Role-Play
- Weapon Neutralization
- Weapon Retention
- OC Aerosol Subject Restraint

Lectures Seminars Training

Topics Include

Ten Tips for Assault and
Rape Prevention and Role-Playing

Choosing and Using a Weapon for Self-Protection

Child Lures and Children's Sexual Assault
Prevention Workshop for Parents and Their Children

1-800-467-1900

Currently In the Works

Other Books by
BO HARDY

Working Titles

DEFENSIVE LIVING FOR KIDS
How to Avoid Abduction and Victimization

DEFENSIVE LIVING WEAPONS
Choosing and Using a Weapon for Self-Protection

- More than 90 percent of sexual assaults involve one victim and one assailant.

- Date and acquaintance rapes account for more than half of all sexual assaults.

- The practice of assigning two police officers per patrol car rather than one officer per car significantly reduces the occurrence of physical assaults directed toward police officers.

- The military victory over Iraq confirmed the effect of strength in numbers. By not attacking Iraqi targets until United States forces overwhelmingly outnumbered Iraqi troops and weapons strengths, the U. S. in effect had psychologically defeated Iraq before the fight began.

- Many animals instinctively group together for self-preservation, especially those that have no natural weapons for defense.

- Most predatory animals will instinctively seek the easiest prey available: One that shows fear when confronted, one that is young and ignorant of the dangers of straying from the herd, or one too old or sick to keep up with the group. Even the ferocious tiger will attack a stray before confronting the herd.

- The buddy system is just as important for men as it is for women and children. Many male corporate executives and politicians are kidnapped for ransom, and the vast majority are alone when abducted. Many are never found alive.

The "animals" you face are no different than those in the wild. They prey on the easiest victim they can find. And more often than not, the victim chosen is a lone victim. All of those examples emphasize and reinforce one important crime prevention tip: Being in a group or close to other people significantly reduces your chances of being criminally victimized.

WHY THE BUDDY SYSTEM IS SO EFFECTIVE

THERE IS STRENGTH IN NUMBERS

A mugger, rapist or abductor is much less likely to confront a group of people than one person alone. An assailant's chances of success are reduced considerably in the presence of more than one person. There are also more people to identify him. If there are more people to resist his demands, he could easily become the "victim."

The predator/prey roles might easily be reversed if he were to attack a group. Why would he take a chance of meeting resistance from others in the group when there are plenty of "strays" available?

If an assailant plans to kidnap or sexually assault his intended victim, he is looking for only one person. He is similar to an animal predator searching for a victim. You don't see an animal predator attack three victims for a meal.

You won't see a mountain lion attack a bear cub unless the mother bear is absent. Likewise, an assailant is seldom going to attempt an abduction of a child unless that child is alone or isolated. The innate drive of parents to protect their young is just as powerful as any animal's instinct to protect their young, and assailants are aware of that. That is why it is critical for children to always use the buddy system.

Whether an assault is successful or not, in choosing a lone victim, an assailant knows that if arrested, it often comes down to his word against the victim's. Without witnesses, it is much more difficult to prove that a particular person was indeed the assailant or if a crime was actually committed.

Hospitals, exercise studios and store parking lots are notorious as prime locations for abductions. Never be on a parking lot alone when walking to or from your vehicle. Organize or agree to always accompany friends or fellow co-workers to their vehicles.

Grocery stores have become "the place" for single men and women to meet, especially at night. Always go with a friend, since this is a dangerous way to meet new friends. Most assailants seek their prey alone, and what better place to find prey than at a grocery store? It is easy to avoid one of the most traumatic crimes anyone will experience by taking just a little time to work out a way to stay in a group or use other people.

If you are encouraged or required by your employer to park in the distant parking spaces so customers can park closer to the store entrance, it is even more important that you use the buddy system when walking to your car.

There is a sense of security and power for those in a group or around other people. They provide someone to counsel with and they increase one's confidence, even when a wrong decision is made.

THE BUDDY SYSTEM IS EFFECTIVE NOT ONLY AGAINST CRIMINALS, BUT ALSO OTHER ANIMALS

An elderly woman was attacked by two dogs as she returned to her home from her neighbor's. When found, she had been knocked down by two German shepherd dogs and had been severely bitten and mangled. A neighbor had only to use a verbal command to shoo the dogs away.

Neither the owner of the dogs nor any of the investigating officers could understand what provoked the dogs, which had never attacked anyone before. The dogs were subsequently destroyed, and the woman recovered after an extended convalescence.

After studying the details of the incident, it was obvious to me what could have prevented the attack. There were two dogs and one woman. Had there been only one dog, I feel certain the attack wouldn't have occurred.

The victim was alone. Had she been accompanied by someone, the attack most likely would not have occurred.

The victim was quite elderly. Had she been younger, I would bet the dogs would not have attacked. Dogs can instinctively sense when someone is afraid, old and weak, or young and frail.

The victim was not carrying anything that could be used as a weapon, such as a cane or purse. Animals can sense instinctively if a person is armed. If you don't believe it, the next time a dog barks or threatens, act as if you are picking up a rock and watch its reaction. Animals are much smarter than we give them credit for.

The incident was a classic case of predators/prey. Only this time, the predators — not the victim — used the buddy system.

HOW TO USE THE BUDDY SYSTEM WHEN ALONE

Obviously, you can't always have a buddy with you. Many people live alone or often have to shop or travel alone. There are other ways to use the system even when you prefer to be, or out of necessity have to be, alone.

WHEN SHOPPING

You should always wait for others to get out of their vehicles before leaving your locked car. When leaving a mall entrance to approach your car, never walk out alone. Wait for others to leave the store at the same time you do and use them as your buddy. It is worth waiting thirty seconds or so for others, especially at night.

For those of you who like to shop and buy your groceries late at night to avoid the crowds, reconsider. There is a great deal of safety in those long lines and crowded parking lots. Yes, it's annoying and time-consuming to shop at the busiest times of day, but so is being mugged or kidnapped. Try to develop a new outlook about the crowds you have despised in the past.

A high percentage of sexual assaults (sixty percent to eighty percent) occur at night. Darkness provides the advantages of surprise and cover, and fewer people are out at night, so there are fewer witnesses to the crime.

Be careful not to dine out late at night. Closing time is a prime time for many armed robberies, which tend to be violent crimes. Many murders occur in late-night restaurant robberies. Be smart and eat early, when it's crowded and much safer.

If you doubt the importance of the buddy system, think about the "gang" situation we are faced with. There are gangs in cities with populations of 2,000 and less. Why do you think members join a gang in the first place? Security and a sense of power. Many gang members are insecure people and find security in belonging to a group. Even gangs use the buddy system. You should learn to if you don't already.

If the assailant is deranged or drugged enough to attack or confront a group of people, do not escalate the situation. Such people are often violent and unpredictable and they may be desperate enough to do anything to feed their needs.

If you are with a group and are approached by an assailant, comply with his demands and do as little as possible to aggravate the situation. The only demand you must not comply with is that you go with him. I will discuss options for that situation in Tip 9.

IMPORTANCE OF THE BUDDY SYSTEM FOR YOUR CHILDREN

Assailants seek the easiest victims and children are quite often the target. You can't read a newspaper without reading of a child being abducted somewhere in the United States. Ninety-nine percent of the time, the child is alone when abducted. The same prevention principles apply for children as for adults. Make sure your child is always with another child or a group of children when playing or attending youth functions.

Never let your children sell Girl Scout cookies, Little League candy, school raffle tickets or other items alone. Always accompany them or make sure they have a friend accompany them, even in your own neighborhood.

Your neighborhood may be crime-free, but that doesn't keep a criminal from driving through even an upper-class neighborhood and in a matter of minutes, totally changing your and your child's lives forever.

ENCOURAGE THE BUDDY SYSTEM FOR YOUR TEENAGERS

Date and acquaintance rapes account for approximately half the rapes reported. Encourage your teenagers to not go out on "single" dates, especially when it is a first date. Insist that your children go on dates accompanied by others the first few times and agree to meet at a public place, until you and your child know the person. By insisting that your child meet the date at a public restaurant or theater, the child doesn't have to rely on the date for transportation home.

Encourage your teens to be aware of comments and mannerisms that show dislike or condescension toward the opposite sex. Train your children to listen for dialogue that shows a desire to discuss sex excessively or for any discussion of abuse of the opposite sex or animals. Any comments about physical dominance or hints of aggressive personality should always be noticed.

As parents, you have the responsibility to educate your teenagers about such characteristics and save them the agony of finding out after the fact how dangerous single dating can be. The incidence of rape on college campuses is so under-reported that federal legislation has been written and approved requiring crimes on college campuses to be reported by the institution and statistics made available to the public.

Strength in numbers means your child is less likely to be victimized by a date or other assailant.

BABY-SITTING

Never let your young son or daughter baby-sit alone. One of my closest friend's fifteen-year-old daughter was raped while doing so.

The yardman for the family heard the couple say they were going out and realized they would have a baby sitter coming that evening. He watched until the couple left, then broke in on the girl as she slept with the infant. Her first sexual experience was that of being raped by someone who had been convicted of many sex crimes, unknown to the couple who had hired him.

There is also a threat to the young infant or child who is being tended. There are incidents every day where a teenager molests, rapes or kills the young child being tended. Even when you think you know a particular teen or adult you use for baby-sitting, it is still wise to insist or recommend they bring a friend.

A ten-year-old girl was raped and murdered by her sixteen-year-old cousin. The cousin had recently moved in with her family because he was having some discipline problems.

Rather than continue to hire a baby sitter, the ten-year-old's mother decided to let the cousin tend the child. In a fit of anger, the boy raped and strangled the girl. It was later discovered that his parents were aware of his violent temper and sexual problems, but failed to tell his aunt.

Many sex crimes occur when children are left alone with older relatives, and many are never reported.

By allowing a friend to accompany your child when baby-sitting, you can also prevent an assault by one of the adults who hired the sitter.

Never permit one parent to drive your son or daughter home alone late at night after baby-sitting. There have been many instances of children being raped or molested by an adult who perhaps had too much to drink or who saw an opportunity to victimize a child when alone.

It isn't always an adult male victimizing a teenage female. It can be an adult female victimizing a young male.

A woman I work with recently encountered such an incident. Her fourteen-year-old son was dating a girl his age, and the mother of the girl began calling the boy to ask him to visit more often. The young boy finally confided to his mother that the woman had made several sexual advances toward him and had told him she was in love with him.

The mental impact this kind of incident can have on any child, whether male or female, can affect them for the rest of their lives. The parents of teenagers must be aware of those possibilities and always try to keep the buddy system in mind to prevent such incidents.

WHEN LETTING YOUR CHILDREN BABY-SIT

Make sure you know the name and address of the people your children are baby-sitting for.

It is hard to believe, but parents often allow their children to baby-sit for people they vaguely know. If an emergency were to occur, be able to tell the police where and for whom your children are baby-sitting.

Make sure your children know the full name of the people they are working for and the address where they are baby-sitting.

If an emergency were to occur, make sure they know how to get assistance, such as fire, police and medical attention. Many small towns are not equipped with 911 emergency telephone service. Trying to get medical or police assistance to an address unknown by your baby-sitting children could cause a life-threatening situation for either your children or the child being tended.

OTHER BUDDIES

The buddy system can also mean having a self-protection weapon as your "buddy" if you can't be with other people.

One of the best buddies you can have is a dog. They are excellent protection in or out of the house. When traveling or walking, a dog is not only a close companion, but also one of the best deterrents against crime. Interviews with convicted burglars and muggers confirm that someone accompanied by a dog or a dog's presence in a house was the number one reason they chose not to attempt a crime.

Many convicted burglars have stated that they would not even consider burglarizing a home with a dog either in the house or yard. Most professional burglars will always choose a home with an alarm system over one with a guard dog.

They know exactly where to look for valuables and how much time they have and will have already planned a route of escape. The professional burglar knows the only barrier to completing his crime is time and will know exactly how much time he has to escape.

Even when the alarm is activated, he knows he generally has from ten to fifteen minutes. He can wipe you out and be gone by the time the police arrive. And it is wishful thinking to assume the police will arrive in that amount of time.

Sometimes, just having a weapon visible will deter an assailant from choosing you as his victim. One good example of this is a tie tack in the shape of a pair of handcuffs. A potential assailant will be the first to notice the tie tack. And of course, you know what he will automatically assume. What would you think if someone approached you wearing a tie with a pair of handcuffs for a tie tack? That he is a police officer. Ex-convicts and criminals always try to avoid the law enforcement officer.

I recently counseled a home health care nurse whose job requires her to travel to homes in a crime-ridden part of a city. She had been confronted several times by questionable characters. She is not allowed to carry a firearm and can be fired for even having one in her car while on hospital business.

Her frustration and apprehension about her safety were understandable. So I equipped her with a few buddies. Now when she gets out of her car and has to walk in those neighborhoods, she has a

pair of handcuffs hanging from under her jacket just visible enough to look as if she doesn't want them to be seen. She wears a pistol holster with only the bottom half exposed. But she is the only one who knows the holster is empty.

She recently told me she hasn't even been whistled at lately, much less harassed as she once was on a daily basis. She loves it when onlookers ask questions like, "Hey lady, are you a cop?" Her reply is always the same. "What do you think I am, a nurse?" She didn't lie. She said that few street people even speak anymore.

The success of such role-play is based on the premise that most criminals want to avoid contact with anyone they think would be in the law enforcement profession. Most of them have been in trouble with the law many times, and quite often are being sought on outstanding warrants.

If the nurse were to be harassed, a good role to assume would be that of a parole officer looking for someone with a name she has preplanned. Even worse than accidentally mugging a police officer is the assailant's fear of encountering a parole officer, because the parole officer doesn't even need an excuse or warrant to enter a home and take a parole violator into custody.

Her buddies in this case happen to be rather innovative, but effective. What may sound like a silly ploy has become a necessity for many to avoid the rising epidemic of assaults.

I will discuss other forms of self-protection weapons that can be considered a buddy in Tip 6.

BUDDIES WHO DON'T EXIST, BUT PROTECT YOU

In 500 B.C., during one of many battles waged in China, a general was given the order by his commander to lay siege to a town protected by ten thousand opposing soldiers. His troops numbered only one thousand.

The town to be attacked was on a hill, and there was no way to approach the target without first exposing his forces. Since he was outnumbered ten to one, he had to devise a plan that relied on outsmarting his enemy rather than outfighting him. The valley below the town was in clear view of the defending forces and was surrounded by mountains, with only a narrow path leading into it. There was no chance of surprising the defending forces.

The general ordered his troops to begin entering the valley single file at dusk and immediately set up their tents and build their campfires. He wanted to ensure that his troops were still entering the valley as it turned dark, for the opposing forces to see. The opposing general and his troops watched from above as the attacking army made camp and began to build their campfires.

Hours after darkness had fallen, the defending troops and their general became increasingly concerned as they watched thousands of campfires being built. Before midnight, the entire valley was ablaze with campsites and more troops were arriving by the hour as campfires were lit in every corner of the valley. By 3:00 a.m., the defending forces counted more than 50,000 campfires.

The defending general, fearing total annihilation, ordered his troops to abandon their stations and retreat. By dawn, the defending forces had fled the town and were in fast retreat. The general of the attacking forces sent spies into the town to determine if his "siege" had succeeded. Upon hearing that the defenders had fled, he allowed his one thousand troops to sleep the rest of the day before entering the now-undefended city. They had earned the rest by building so many fires during the night.

Twenty-five hundred years later, an elderly woman, confronted by an armed assailant at her front door, immediately turned and yelled toward her upstairs, "Tom, John. Get the shotgun and come quick. Someone's trying to rob me." The assailant, thinking he had obviously picked the wrong person to rob, hastily fled, having no idea that there was no "Tom," "John" or "shotgun" in the house.

Somewhere, an ancient Chinese general was smiling proudly as he

watched the elderly woman successfully defend herself using her imaginary buddies.

Many documented cases detail how people have used their intelligence and ingenuity when confronted by an assailant or assailants, by seeking assistance from their imaginary buddies. People have been using this method for more than twenty-five hundred years and it's still effective.

GET TO KNOW YOUR IMAGINARY BUDDIES BEFOREHAND

About ten years ago, I was awakened at 2:00 a.m. by a woman banging on my front door. When I went to the door and looked out the blinds, the woman pleaded, "Help, open the door, someone is after me." I'm not really sure why I didn't open the door, but there was something unconvincing about the way she was pleading for assistance.

I told her to stay at the door while I called the police and got my shotgun. As I closed the blinds and started for the phone, I heard her whisper, "He's calling the police and getting a shotgun, let's get the ... out of here."

I quickly opened the blinds and saw her two male companions, who had been hiding at the corner of my house. All three ran to their car, which was parked just out of sight on the street. I had a difficult time getting back to sleep that night.

I had developed a plan of action for such an event. That ruse is a common one to gain access to your home. The dilemma presented is that while you don't want to neglect someone who is in legitimate need of help, at the same time you surely don't want to be duped into setting yourself up for victimization.

By using my buddies, even though they were fictitious, I was able to determine if the woman's need was genuine. By waiting for just a few seconds to see the reaction of the "victim" when I told her of my plans, I avoided becoming the victim myself.

That one experience made a lasting impression on me, and I will have my imaginary buddies with me if they are ever needed again.

Many of the crimes I write about in this book involve trickery or subterfuge on the part of the assailant. The more actual situations you are exposed to, the better prepared you can be when faced with a similar situation.

OTHER WAYS TO USE
IMAGINARY BUDDIES

Be cautious about giving information to someone coming to your door or calling on the phone and specifically asking to speak to your husband, "the man of the house" or your wife. If you do live alone, never let the person inquiring know that. Advise him or her that your spouse, your imaginary buddy, is a police officer and is asleep.

Then ask for a business card if the person is at your door or a phone number if he has called. Advise the person that you will have your spouse call when he (she) awakens. Many sexual assaults occur simply because people don't realize how much information an assailant can learn with just a few questions. Always think before you speak. Have a standard answer prepared for the unsolicited calls you receive. Remember **Tip 1, Don't Think and Look Like a Victim.**

The best buddy you have is yourself. When there is no one else to help you, learn to rely on yourself to develop your own methods of outsmarting criminals.

I have shown you several ways to incorporate **Tip 3, Always Use the Buddy System** into your assault prevention plan. It is one of the most effective crime deterrents there is. Please begin to use this tip to help you and your family, especially your children, avoid the terrible effects of assault.

4

Tip 4

Take 15 to 30 Seconds to Observe Your Destination Area Before Approaching

It had just turned dusk. After locking her door, the woman stood at the balcony of her second-floor apartment, taking a few seconds for her eyes to adjust to the darkness. As she observed the area near her locked car, she noticed a man casually walking between cars. As he walked near hers, he stepped into the light on the parking lot and looked up at the woman. She returned his gaze, saying nothing. Then he slowly walked away out of sight. She had never seen the man before, but had no reason to be overly concerned.

Months before, she might not even have noticed him until she reached her car. But now, after attending one of my seminars, she had what she described as a "heightened" sense of awareness. Not paranoia, just perceptiveness.

Rather than continue her planned route to her car, she decided to go back in her apartment, call the security manager for the apartment complex and request that he drive through the area. Within minutes, the security manager arrived and assured her that everything appeared to be safe and there was no sign of anyone loitering in the area. She then completed her uneventful trip to the grocery store.

The next day, she received a call from the security manager thanking her for calling the evening before. He had decided to drive through the adjacent parking areas of the other apartment complexes on the same property. There he discovered the man she had described, standing in the shadows of a stairway.

When the man could provide no identification or reason for being on the property, the security manager detained him until the police arrived. It was then discovered that he had been paroled from prison just two days before. He had an extensive criminal history of sexual assault, kidnapping and other violent crimes for which he had been jailed the last twenty years.

What was even more interesting was the man's first statement to the police after being arrested: "Thank you, you just kept me from committing another horrible crime I would have regretted the rest of my life. Please get me some help."

TAKE 15 TO 30 SECONDS TO OBSERVE YOUR DESTINATION AREA BEFORE APPROACHING

The first few times I presented my Ten Tips for assault prevention, I considered removing this information and replacing the tip with another. But each time, someone in the audience comments about how either they or someone they know has been assaulted simply because they didn't follow **Tip 4.**

Taking 15 to 30 Seconds to Observe Your Destination Area Before Approaching is one of the more difficult tips to incorporate into your daily habits, for several reasons. We all have a tendency to be in such a rush nowadays, so preoccupied with other concerns, that we don't take a few seconds to observe our destination area until we are there. We also make the false assumption that nothing is going to happen to us while we are walking to or from our car.

I recently failed to follow this tip, and I can assure you it won't happen again. I did exactly what I tell everyone not to do and almost

became a victim myself.

I left a department store at a local mall and did not observe the area near my locked vehicle before approaching. I was much more worried about whether the sales clerk had given me the right amount of change than I was about being criminally victimized that day (at least my car was locked). What could possibly happen in the middle of the afternoon on a crowded parking lot? And besides, assault prevention "experts" don't have to worry about being victimized. We are ready for anything.

I was almost to my car when I looked up for the first time (critical mistake) to see a police officer, gun in hand, running toward me from my left. As he pointed his gun at me, I quickly wondered, what in the world have I done? At that same instant, he yelled for me to get down, which I did immediately. It was only when I fell to the ground that I noticed the person to my right pointing a pistol at the police officer. I had been standing between the two.

Had I taken even 10 to 15 seconds to observe the area near my car, I would have seen several police cars and officers silently converging on the area. I was fortunate not to have been injured, taken hostage or shot that day. The only damage done was to my inflated sense of invincibility. I am again using this tip without exception after that incident. I have relived that incident many times mentally, and I think about how ironic it was that even I had thought something like that could never happen to me — until it did.

I have had many calls from seminar members saying this tip has prevented them from becoming a victim of crime. I will continue to include it as one of the ten most important to follow to avoid being victimized. The more you realize how important this advice really is in preventing you from becoming a victim of crime, the easier it will become to take those few seconds to observe your surroundings.

Like the other tips, once it becomes a habit, it will be difficult *not* to take a few seconds to observe your destination area before approaching. This is another one of those tips that, once developed, is easy to incorporate into your daily habits and takes no special skills to use.

LOOK FOR THE UNUSUAL

Before leaving the safety of a department store, grocery store, fitness center, etc. where there are others nearby, always observe the area near your locked vehicle before approaching. Look for any unusual activity near your vehicle. If you notice others near your car, wait until they leave. It is quite common for people to be assaulted as they get in or out of their vehicles. This is not the time to first notice that someone is standing by your car.

If you are still in your locked vehicle, before leaving wait that few seconds to let them pass or enter their car. Why take a chance when all it takes is a few seconds of patience to perhaps avoid being victimized? Remember from Tip 2: your car can be a barrier or trap depending on how you use it.

WHAT TO DO
WHEN FOLLOWED

If you have just walked out of a store, and someone is standing near the entrance, pause, make eye contact and speak. You can determine in those few seconds if it is wise to continue your walk to your car or if you should return to the safety of the store and ask security personnel to escort you. If it just doesn't feel quite right, trust your intuition and return immediately.

You must determine in the first few steps of your journey if you are being followed. If so, then is the time to find out, rather than when you arrive at your car. The farther you distance yourself from the safety of others, the greater your chances of being assaulted.

Many people have told me of being victimized as they were followed to their car from a store. And their comment was always the same. Many have said they quickened their walk when they realized they were being followed. They didn't know anything else to do but continue to their car. That is the last thing to do. Remember **Tip 1, Don't Look Like a Victim**. That is exactly what you are doing if you hurry.

One of the best ways to determine if you are being followed is to turn slightly to the side and pretend to gaze at the sky or look down and pretend you dropped something, while also observing the area behind you. If you are being followed, then is the time to turn around, go back toward the area you just left and while passing the person, snap your fingers, make eye contact and mumble aloud, as though you are talking to yourself, something like, "I left my billfold at the cash register!"

Look at everything you have just accomplished.

You are no longer walking toward your car wondering if you are being followed while listening to your heart thump with the fear of being assaulted. You are walking back toward a safe area. You have also made eye contact and spoken, thus becoming proactive rather than reactive. And in a brief but effective way you have engaged in active role-play. If the person did intend to rob or assault you, what kind of victim do you look like now? One without a billfold to steal.

Go back in and request store security to escort you to your vehicle. Or find the manager and tell him that if he doesn't do something about the safety of his parking lot, you will shop at another store.

Always try to park as close to the entrance as possible. It is worth the 15 to 30 seconds to circle the parking lot one more time to find a space closer to the entrance. Remember the predator/prey concept. Don't look like a lone, isolated victim. If you feel threatened by circumstances, park in the handicapped area temporarily and tell the store management you are "mentally" handicapped because of the poor lighting in the parking area or the groups of youths hanging around. Tell store officials to either make the area safer or lose your business.

Unless you make business owners aware of your concerns, they won't react. If they think it might cost them some business, perhaps they will realize how important a safe shopping environment is to customers. Malls have become "the" hangout for youth gangs. Some mall managers are realizing that there are some things even more important than sale prices to their customers.

Always park so that your driver's side faces the entrance of your destination. Parking with the driver's side away from the entrance makes it difficult to observe and gives an assailant the advantage.

BE OBSERVANT THE ENTIRE TIME YOU ARE WALKING TO OR FROM YOUR LOCKED VEHICLE

The sooner you are aware something might be amiss, the more time you have to plan your course of action. Even if you notice someone only seconds before approaching your car or home, that still gives you the valuable time to locate your "weapon," whether it be your car key or your role-play ability to prepare to defend yourself.

You can be a 10th Degree black belt in karate and still be hit by someone if you don't see the punch coming. It is hard to block something you don't see. Likewise, it is hard to defend yourself against an assailant you never see until it is too late. The assailant may not be following you but hiding nearby or in another vehicle near yours.

OBSERVING YOUR HOME

When arriving at home, observe the surroundings for any suspicious movement and always make a quick inventory of doors and windows to ensure no obvious intrusion has taken place.

When arriving at your house or your apartment, take a few seconds before getting out of your vehicle, especially at night, to let your eyes adjust to the darkness after turning your headlights off. Don't open the door to your car and then begin to gather everything you plan to take in with you. Plan the short trip from your safe location to your next safe location. If you live in an apartment complex, observe other cars nearby for occupants before getting out of your car.

DON'T ENTER A
BURGLARIZED HOUSE

I am still surprised at the number of people who admit that they did not realize their home had been broken into until they reached the front door and discovered it standing open. They say they never even looked toward the door of their home before leaving their vehicle. And when I ask people what they did after discovering their door open, the majority say they went in to determine what was missing.

One woman recently told of discovering her front door open and, after entering, meeting the burglar as he walked out with her stereo. She said he just stared at her and walked right by and out the door. Thankfully for her, she did nothing but stare in disbelief and close the door after he left.

Always make a quick inventory of all doors and windows as you approach your home or apartment while still in your car. You should never enter your home if it appears to have been broken into. If everything appears to be secure, it is a prudent practice to still take that 15 to 30 seconds to observe the area around your home and car before leaving your vehicle.

Before you leave your home or apartment, always try to leave a light on if you know you will be arriving after dark.

If you are fortunate enough to have an enclosed garage, it is still wise to always look in your car before entering. This is so obvious that it shouldn't be included in this book, but I still talk to people at seminars who admit they never look in their cars before getting in.

Taking 15 to 30 seconds to observe may seem like an unnecessary habit to develop, but how much effort does it take to become a little more observant? If it keeps you or a family member from becoming a victim of assault one time, then your efforts will have been well worth it.

BE PERCEPTIVE WHILE WALKING OR DRIVING

Develop the habit of consciously looking at your immediate surroundings while walking or driving. I shudder every time I pass someone running or walking at night wearing headphones. That's looking like a victim. By the time you can hear someone approaching you from the side or behind, it will be far too late to plan a course of action.

A young girl was recently attacked by a gang of boys as she walked home from a neighbor's house after baby-sitting. They had dragged her between two houses and were about to rape her when a man drove by and just happened to be observing the entire area, and not merely the street in front of him. It was obvious to the man that something very wrong was taking place, and he turned around and went to the girl's aid. Just by being observant of his surroundings, he saved the girl from a horrible ordeal.

When driving, try to be observant of your surroundings not only for your sake but for other possible victims of crime. If your habit of being observant saves one person from the horrors of being victimized, you will have given yourself a reward for all time.

By being observant while driving, you can allow yourself those precious few seconds to change your direction in case you see an accident ahead or, worse, an assailant about to strike.

AUTOMATIC TELLER MACHINES CAN BE DANGEROUS TO YOUR HEALTH

Using bank machines at night is almost like painting a bulls-eye on your forehead. If you must frequent the machines after hours, take extreme precautions and certainly take the 15 to 30 seconds to observe this destination area before approaching.

The use of automatic teller machines for after-hours banking has become extremely dangerous in the last few years. In one state, at least a half-dozen murders have occurred after people were abducted and robbed at the machines. Unless extreme security measures are taken, these machines will go the way of the manual typewriter. Even though many ATM sites are well-lighted, a criminal has only to wait in hiding and follow the intended victim to his next stop if he doesn't want to risk a confrontation at the ATM site.

That is a common method of operation for robbers. Make it a habit to leave the area as soon as possible and be especially alert for a possible assailant following you. I will further discuss the action to be taken if followed in Tip 7.

Few people take the time to observe their destination area before approaching. As I pointed out at the beginning of this chapter, this tip is one habit that will take a conscious effort to develop. It is similar to getting into the habit of wearing a seat belt. Initially, a conscious effort is needed to "buckle up" for safety. But it takes only one accident when the seat belt saved your life for you to feel the habit was worth the effort. **Tip 4, Take 15 to 30 Seconds to Observe Your Destination Area Before Approaching**, is a form of buckling up. The one time you fail to follow the tip could prove fatal.

5

Tip 5

If You Decide to Physically Resist Your Assailant, Do So Only to Avoid Personal Injury or Death

In New York City, a woman was waiting for the subway when someone approached her and attempted to steal her purse. She began to fight with her attacker, refusing to relinquish the purse. The mugger, in a fit of fury, finally wrenched away her purse and shoved her in front of the approaching subway. She was killed and the assailant was captured by witnesses. When the woman's purse was searched for valuables, it was found to contain one dollar. She had given up her life for a dollar!

I have documented hundreds of true stories where a victim was severely injured or killed over material possessions. I am amazed at the number of reports I still read in the newspapers or see on television where innocent victims refuse to relinquish their purse or wallet and are killed or seriously injured.

Material possessions are not worth risking your life! I know of instances where an attacker has cut or bitten off a victim's fingers for jewelry, including fake jewelry that merely looked expensive. Being victimized is very humiliating and infuriating, but remember, material possessions can be replaced. You can't!

Sometimes our personalities make it difficult to give up what we know is rightfully ours. And sometimes, we don't use our heads and make foolish judgments.

FIGHT OR FLIGHT?

The fight-or-flight, resist-or-not-resist controversy has existed forever. Anyone who professes to know what you should do in every situation is just talking to hear himself. Each situation or confrontation is so different that there is no way to give a standard answer of "yes, you should always resist" or "no, you should do whatever the assailant tells you to do."

THREE FACTORS IN DETERMINING A COURSE OF ACTION

1. THE PERSONALITY OF THE VICTIM

In one recent seminar I conducted, a woman told of how infuriated she became upon seeing her car being driven out of her driveway by a thief. Before she thought about what she was doing, she ran out her front door and chased her stolen car down the street, screaming at the top of her lungs for the thief to stop.

Even though months had passed, retelling the incident brought tears to her eyes. I asked her what she would have done had she caught up with the thief. Still boiling, she stated, "I have no idea, but I sure would like to have found out!" A very large, muscular man sitting next to her responded, "Lady, you're crazy! I wouldn't have done anything but lock my front door and call the police! People are too crazy nowadays."

One important factor in planning a course of action is being aware

of your own personality. Are you a "Type A" personality, naturally aggressive in everything you do? If so, you are going to have a natural tendency to fight no matter how trivial the confrontation. There are times when resisting will get you killed, as with the woman waiting for the subway. This can be as dangerous as being on the other end of the personality spectrum, a "Type B," who never resists when confronted.

If you happen to be very passive and would normally give up your valuables when confronted, you may not be hurt most of the time. But when the confrontation is a life-or-death situation, you may wish to take on a little of the aggressive personality.

Don't allow your personality to escalate the trouble with your assailant. Try to temper your personality toward the opposite tendency. If you are naturally passive, try to become a little stronger in your convictions. If you tend to be the expressive, driven type, like the woman who chased after her stolen car, you might temper your tendency to immediately "attack" and perhaps first think what would be the wise thing to do.

One of the main reasons women are a prime target for sexual assault, abuse, etc., is the perception that the female is a much weaker, more submissive subject than a male. In the past, young girls were taught to be submissive and stay in what was socially considered to be the "woman's role." I hope this limited view is a thing of the past.

Not only women, but men and children are tired of being afraid to even venture out into their front yards.

2. THE PERSONALITY OF THE ASSAILANT

In addition to being aware of your own personality type, it is just as important to try to determine the type of assailant you are dealing with, and to do it in those first few seconds of confrontation. What does this person want to gain from the confrontation? Does he want just your valuables? If so, give them as quickly and quietly as possible. Or does he want your valuables and to inflict physical and mental harm on you?

For example, there are generally four types of violent criminals;

those who act through (1) a need for reassurance, (2) ego, (3) anger, (4) sadism. These four profiles apply to most criminals, from a car thief to a rapist or child molester. The first level of criminal, the "reassure-me" assailant, is the least violent. He tends to be very insecure. You can defeat him fairly easily by (a) refusing to succumb to his demands and using verbal counteraction, such as screaming or threatening, or (b) choosing to physically resist and using physical counteraction.

On the other end of the scale is the sadistic criminal, the most dangerous type of assailant to confront. Verbally refusing his commands will often elicit only a smile from him, or possibly a violent, damaging blow. Shout or scream at him and you will likely be knocked unconscious, and possibly found later having been sexually assaulted and bludgeoned to death. With the sadistic assailant, you must determine a course of action that will not escalate the confrontation and will provide a safe means of escape.

We are all very different, both victim and assailant, and to predict the level of conflict between any two individuals in a confrontation is like taking two unknown chemicals and predicting the degree of explosion if you were to mix them together. It is best to avoid mixing the "chemicals." If you are unable to do so, knowing as much as possible about both before the event and developing a safe plan can help you survive the "explosion."

It is very difficult to rely on a single plan of action for all confrontations. If the assailant appears to be drunk or on drugs and is slow to react to your responses, your chances of successfully using some form of resistance may increase. You may be able to outthink your attacker because of his altered mental state. Your chances of using some form of physical force may successfully increase thanks to his lack of coordination and motor skills.

However, it quite often can be very dangerous to attempt to counterattack unless you are extremely proficient in the method planned. In many cases when individuals are under the influence of drugs, their pain threshold does not seem to exist. They are able to withstand debilitating and lethal injuries they could never survive normally. Many of the violent criminals you are likely to encounter are influenced by drugs and alcohol. Physical counteraction takes much more proficiency than one is led to believe in karate and self-defense courses. I strongly recommend that you never try to physically defeat

this kind of assailant without some form of self-protection weapon, such as a pepper spray.

If you are assaulted, role-play and follow your previously prepared plan of action based on the severity and type of assault. It will be too late to think about options once the assault begins. You must have options already stored in your "mental computer" and ready to use.

There is no single response to all assaults. You must be prepared to respond in the safest, most prudent way to ensure that you survive the confrontation, whether the assailant wants only your valuables or wants your valuables and your life. I will cover options later in this and other chapters as I explain alternatives to assault.

3. LOCATION OF THE ATTACK

Where you are confronted is the third common factor to be considered in deciding how to react to an assault. Are you on a crowded mall parking lot while a serial killer tries to force you into your vehicle? Or are you in the driveway of your residence at 1:00 a.m. when there is no one else nearby?

Your plan of action should be very different in these two situations. The assailant wants to isolate you to complete his crime. The last thing he wants is to attract attention. Speed is critical in his completing the abduction.

If you are on the crowded parking lot, realistically, he is not going to shoot or sexually assault you in front of witnesses. Therefore, you can use forms of passive resistance, such as fainting, dropping to the ground and crawling under a car or screaming. If you scream, use words or phrases like repeating "No" over and over, or "9-1-1." If you shout, "Help! This man has a gun!" many people will run the other way, fearing for their lives.

If you choose to fight, many people will refuse or hesitate to help for fear of being hurt themselves. They tend to avoid interfering in physical altercations, not knowing if the incident is perhaps a marital or personal squabble.

If you are forced into a vehicle on a parking lot, which you should **never** allow to happen, or if someone has forced their way into your car, make sure you never leave the lot. You should **never** leave the public eye.

Want to attract a crowd? Ram into ten cars on that parking lot or crash right through the front entrance to the building when the assailant tells to drive. Everyone within a half-mile will come rushing to see what happened. People will flock to a wreck. The last thing your assailant wants is a crowd. Watch how quickly he tries to blend into the crowd and escape. You will have made him the prey instead of yourself.

In a situation where you are alone or isolated, such as in a parking deck or entering your residence late at night, your options are considerably different. You must defeat your predator, through either mental or physical skills, by yourself. Passive resistance, such as fainting, still may be an alternative; but if the assailant attempts to sexually assault or attack you anyway, then you must rely on some other form of self-defense. In this situation it is critical that you have already role-played and determined your backup course of action. Whether the choice is physical counteraction or the use of a self-protection weapon, you must be mentally and physically prepared to defend yourself.

Much of the time people spend in my seminars is devoted to exploring these alternatives and to choosing those that have an excellent chance of success in enabling them to escape injury or death.

RULES FOR
PHYSICAL COUNTERACTION

Rule 1 — No matter where you are or how serious the confrontation is, the longer you prolong contact with the assailant, the less your chance of escaping serious injury or death.

This is one of the most important rules to follow when planning your course of action. If all your assailant wants are your personal possessions, let him have them immediately. You want the encounter

to be as brief as possible. It is not the time to start asking your assailant if he has considered rehabilitation or counseling or if he has considered going to church! Instead, you might assist him in a safe manner so he can escape more quickly.

Rule 2 — If the assailant threatens you by showing a weapon, don't try to disarm him.

It takes years of intensive training to become proficient in disarming and neutralization tactics. When an assailant is armed and wants only material possessions, make the encounter as brief as possible.

Once the assailant has what he wants, distance yourself from him quickly. If he is armed with a firearm, as you retreat, turn with one side to your assailant to offer a smaller target in case he decides to shoot. Even trained police officers, who have to practice and qualify repeatedly, have a difficult time hitting a person turned sideways and over ten to fifteen feet away.

The wisdom of physical resistance against an armed assailant is very questionable. Only when you feel your life is placed in danger, such as through violent assault or abduction by complying with his demands, should you consider physical resistance. And when physical resistance is chosen, passive resistance, such as pretending to lose consciousness or fainting, should be your preferred method. I will discuss this method in greater detail in Tip 9.

ACTIVE OR
PASSIVE RESISTANCE?

I strongly support the use of passive resistance over physical counteraction or the use of a weapon to defend yourself. It is much more difficult to execute a physical plan of defense than a mental plan.

Self-defense techniques, the use of a firearm and other methods of self-protection are much more difficult to execute under the pressure of an actual assault than in a controlled classroom or firing range environment. Police officers who are experts on the firing range have been known to miss assailants with multiple shots fired from point-blank range. One can see this principle in any sport or contact activity.

In many sports, one can excel in practice or warm-ups only to find that when faced with a formidable opponent, one's ability degenerates quickly. Many of us armchair basketball players can shoot "lights out" in the backyard. But when faced with the real "game" situation and all the pressures that accompany confrontation by an "assailant," the percentage of successful "shots" drops considerably. When the situation becomes real and the stress of confrontation is imminent, it is very difficult to predict what physical course of action we will take and what the results will be.

PHYSICAL SELF-DEFENSE TECHNIQUES

No self-defense book would be complete without at least four hundred ways to kill or maim your opponent with your bare hands and feet. So for those who feel this book must describe physical techniques to offer "real" self-defense, here is your section!

One of the areas in which I have expertise is the study of the effects of physical punishment and damage to the human body through the use of hands and feet. I have fought more people in one night than ninety-nine percent of the general population will fight in a lifetime. I have fought hundreds of karate and taekwondo black belts over the past thirty years. A typical night teaching a sparring class involves sparring with ten to twenty students for five to fifteen minutes each.

I have been punched, kicked, thrown, twisted and stomped on by men and women of all ages, sizes and temperaments. I have had my protective headgear kicked off my head by such karate legends as Bill "Superfoot" Wallace. I have received repeated blows to every part of my anatomy, so I feel very comfortable discussing the effect of physical techniques on the human body and the effectiveness of these techniques when used to defend oneself. I mention this experience not to boast, but rather to substantiate my experience regarding the effects of physical blows.

As a law enforcement trainer and former officer, I have had the opportunity to apply martial arts techniques in many instances where the environment was extremely hostile and subjects were extremely combative, much more so than in a controlled martial arts class. One

learns very quickly which techniques are effective both in karate class and on the street.

It is not only important to know which techniques are the most effective and why. It is just as important, if not more so, to know which techniques are the easiest for a novice to learn and to use effectively. It is best to have quality, not quantity, as your highest priority.

However, you do need to have more than just one or two techniques to rely on in your arsenal, not only for a backup should the expected results fail to occur once you have responded with your counterattack, but also in case you don't have the legal right or desire to inflict serious damage to your assailant.

Your method of counterattack against a family member or acquaintance who perhaps gets too familiar would be very different than against some stranger attempting to abduct you or your child. Just because someone comes along and snatches your purse, you don't have the legal right to catch him and break his neck with a karate chop. I know you might want to, but criminally and civilly, you may wind up as the defendant in a lawsuit for using excessive force.

It is very difficult, if not impossible, to learn physical techniques from a book, even with pictures. Physical techniques take hundreds of hours of practice and must be practiced correctly to become effective. Any discussion of physical technique in a book should be intended as reference material only, and to imply otherwise is gross negligence on the part of the author.

With that disclaimer, I'll discuss some of the techniques I have found to be the most effective on this old battered body of mine and those of many of my martial arts students over the last thirty years.

THREE FACTORS IN CHOOSING A TARGET AREA

1. The effectiveness of an attack to that area.
2. The ease in attacking the area by someone with little training.
3. The difficulty in defending the area by the person attacked.

AREAS TO ATTACK

In determining a target area to counterattack, look for weak areas of the body. It is a fairly simple process to select areas of the anatomy to attack, whether the choice is the use of your hands or feet or the use of some type of self-protection weapon, such as a pepper spray. Even professional athletes who are quite large and intimidating protect certain areas of their massive bodies to prevent possible disabling injuries.

No matter the size, sex or personality of your assailant, there are common areas of vulnerability that all humans share. Think of contact sports like football and basketball. What do professional athletes always protect?

THE EYES

When does a professional boxing match end early and quickly? It won't be from dozens of blows to the head and body from these professionals who train daily trying to develop knockout power. Instead, a thumb or finger to the eye will neutralize even the largest and meanest assailant almost immediately. Basketball, football and other contact sport professionals will tell you the most important area to protect is the eyes. Without your sight, it is very difficult to function normally.

I have been poked in the eyes many times in my fighting career and in teaching assault prevention classes. A finger in one of the eyes begins a rippling effect on the body. It not only makes the eyes water, making it difficult to see, but more importantly, it tends to weaken the entire body. This should be the primary target for temporarily incapacitating an assailant.

Talk with anyone who has ever been poked in the eye while playing basketball, or when playing with a toddler. You instantly realized the effect. Having been injured in the eyes and having accidently hit others in the eyes with a finger or thumb, I know firsthand the effect of this defense, and it is effective. The size of the assailant or the victim is irrelevant. This technique takes very little practice to master.

It is very effective against someone who is on drugs or deranged.

While techniques that rely on pain don't work on some individuals, this one relies on inflaming the tissue and nerves and causing uncontrolled watering of the eyes.

A proper jab to the eyes will provide enough time to escape, and that is your number one objective. Don't hang around and wait to see how much damage you inflicted.

How to Attack the Eyes

When I say attack the eyes, I am not referring to "ripping an assailant's eyeballs out," as you see in many self-defense books. That is much more difficult to do than you are led to believe. All you want to do is jab your first two fingers quickly into the assailant's eyes, withdraw them immediately, and escape.

Take your hand and place your first two fingers on both of your closed eyes. Slowly grip your face, using your thumb on one side and your last two fingers on the other side to help aim, or focus, the first two fingers directly onto both eyes. Squeeze your face and apply pressure to the eyes.

Now, gripping your face again, try lightly tapping your closed eyes with your first two fingers from a few inches away and feel the effect of this technique. Do this a few times until you realize how little force it takes to be effective. Imagine what that would be like with your eyes open. This probably won't permanently blind anyone, but that is not the purpose. Your goal is to strike and escape.

If you are being held

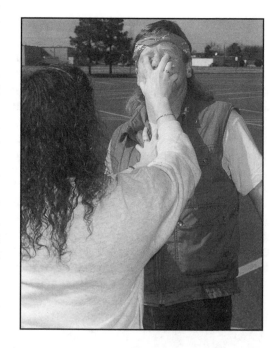

down by an assailant, the technique can be effective for escape because of the temporary blinding it causes. No matter how large or small the assailant is, you always attack weaknesses, not strengths, and all people have this vulnerable area.

It can also be effective to scratch down the face with your fingernails after jabbing the eyes. A deep scratch is one of the more painful wounds and takes a long time to heal. That can provide positive identification of your assailant many days later. Many an assailant has been captured and convicted thanks to scratches or marks left by a victim.

Tips to Remember on Eye Attacks

1. Poke the eyes and retreat.
2. Speed and surprise are crucial in both the execution and escape.
3. They are effective. Even high-ranking black belts and professional boxers, football and basketball players are neutralized temporarily by a little finger to the eye.
4. Self-protection weapons, such as pepper sprays (see Tip 6), are intended to be used against an assailant's eyes.

THE GROIN AREA

What is another of the most damaging and debilitating injuries that can take an athlete out of action? A blow to the groin. Again think of professional fighters and athletes. The groin is another vital area they always cover with protective padding or equipment.

Many books on self-defense discourage attacking the groin area because of the natural tendency of a man to protect this "sacred" area of the body. Let me assure you that most people have a natural tendency to protect any area of their body being attacked.

The groin area is an excellent target and fulfills the three factors in choosing a target area. It is a very sensitive area and even a light blow can incapacitate someone for an extended time. Results of a blow to the groin area can range from doubling over with extreme pain and nausea to death, caused by internal hemorrhaging.

It is a relatively easy target to attack with the knees, and the knee

is one of the most powerful weapons on the human body. Even a light to moderate blow with a knee to the groin will incapacitate the largest of would-be attackers. Quite often in an altercation, the assailant's groin is positioned literally right in front of the victim's knee.

The groin is a difficult area to protect. If an assailant tries to block a knee attack to his groin with his hands, the block is often ineffective. If he does successfully block the

groin attack with his hands, it leaves him with his hands down — and open for the eye attack I discussed earlier.

It is much safer to attack your attacker's groin with your knee rather than with a kick, given the importance of maintaining your balance. The last thing you want to occur is someone grabbing your foot and throwing you off balance. It takes much more coordination to execute a kick to the groin than it does to use the knee.

If somehow you miss the groin with a knee attack, just about anything you strike in the groin area (inner side of thigh, front of thigh, etc.) with your knee can produce a crippling effect long enough and serious enough for you to escape.

Remember, you are looking for ways to protect yourself with little or no training in physical techniques. You don't need hundreds of techniques and dozens of areas to attack, which will just confuse you. Three or four techniques applied to extremely sensitive areas will suffice, allowing you to escape.

Tips to Remember on Groin Attacks

1. It is a technique that is relatively easy to learn and can be practiced without a partner.
2. It is an extremely powerful counterattack because of the use of the large muscle in the thigh.
3. It is effective, even for children, as a technique against a larger adult.
4. A well-placed knee to the groin area gives you the time needed to escape and seek assistance.

THE THROAT

The third area emphasized in my seminars on the use of physical counterattack is the throat. It is very vulnerable to attack and should only be attacked when the threat of serious bodily harm or death is imminent. This too is an area that can be damaged even when the assailant is much larger than you.

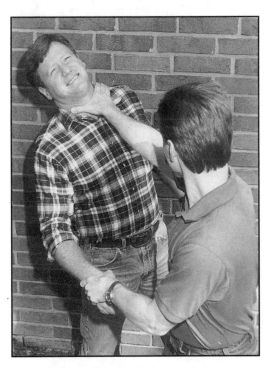

The most practical method for attacking the windpipe and throat is to cup the striking hand, forming a "U." The striking area is the soft part of your hand between your thumb and forefinger, as pictured on this page. A sudden forceful blow to the windpipe in this manner can cause results ranging from temporary choking and coughing to death due to the swelling of traumatized muscles around the windpipe, stopping the flow of oxygen to the lungs and blood to the brain.

The mental effect of this blow to the throat is just as important. The sudden inability to breathe causes temporary paralysis in most people, rendering them immobile for an extended period. This technique also lends itself well for use by those people who are inexperienced in physical counteraction but interested in developing an effective but simple way of causing severe injury to their assailant. It is not a technique to be taken lightly and should be used only to allow you to escape from serious trouble.

A KICKING TECHNIQUE YOU SHOULD KNOW

Because of the difficulty in maintaining one's balance while kicking and the slim chance of hitting a moving target with a kick, I don't recommend many kicking techniques. They take more practice than most people will perform, and they would still create a loss of balance when executed.

WHEN KICKS ARE PRACTICAL

The best time to execute kicking techniques is from a prone position either on the ground or inside an automobile.

THE BICYCLE KICK

Used correctly, this technique will make even the largest and most aggressive assailant think twice before proceeding with the attack. By placing your back against a car door and kicking your assailant repeatedly, as if pedaling

a bicycle, you make it almost impossible to be assaulted and virtually impossible for the assailant to drive the vehicle away.

The power you, or your child, can generate with these kicks will prevent anyone from being able to drive a vehicle for more than a few feet without wrecking or wanting to escape your blows. This kicking method also keeps the assailant away from your vital areas. Women can use this technique very effectively because of their superior lower body strength.

As I mentioned earlier in this chapter, there is no way to teach physical techniques in a book, but I wanted to mention the above techniques since they are included in my seminars, along with a few others I don't publish. These techniques are by no means the only effective ones, but they are fairly easy to develop and maintain for someone who has no plans to continuously practice physical techniques.

TWO CONFRONTATIONAL SITUATIONS

WHEN AWAKENED BY AN INTRUDER IN YOUR HOME

One of the most frightening experiences for anyone is to awaken and realize that an intruder is in the home. If you are like me, when I first awaken, I am lucky if I can find the floor, much less try to think about what to do. Don't wait until this happens to you before deciding a course of action or possible alternatives.

People have done a lot of damage to the interior of their homes by awakening to a noise and shooting at any sound they hear, only to find it was nothing more than a picture falling off a shelf or wall. Who hasn't had some unknown noise waken them in the middle of the night? Scared the heck out of you, did it not?

Your primary objective is to escape your home and not allow it to become a trap. You should have a plan to escape an intruder or assailant just as you should to escape a fire.

When you first awaken, you must take 15 to 30 seconds, as I discussed in Tip 4, to make sure you are not dreaming. Lie there to let your eyes and brain focus. If you are sure someone is in the house and you are not in a position to escape, remain motionless. If they do not approach you, do nothing that might escalate the severity of the situation. If all they want is valuables and not you, then let them go.

If you have a phone next to your bed, make sure you have already programmed 911 into your speed dialer, so that with the push of one button, you can dial 911. If you are afraid you will alert the intruder by talking on the phone, remain quiet. Calling 911 will get an emergency response, even without talk, just as if you were verbally calling for help.

Being approached by an intruder or awakened by an assailant is probably one of the most difficult situations to resolve. There is no one answer to fit all circumstances. The main danger is your inability to function sensibly after having just been awakened.

An armed assailant further complicates the situation. The sensible thing to do at this point is to comply with his demands until you sense you can take some form of defensive action. Whether that action is the use of a weapon, such as a self-protection spray that you have under your pillow, or the use of physical counteraction or passive resistance, such as fainting, now is the time to prepare for the event. Don't wait until the incident occurs to have a plan of action.

WALKING IN ON AN INTRUDER

If you discover, upon arriving, that your home has been broken into, do not enter. Go to a neighbor's or nearby pay phone and call the police. Believe it or not, many people will enter their residence after discovering a door or window open, not having any idea if the intruder is still on the premises. Some of those people have not lived to talk about it.

If you confront an intruder when entering or once inside your residence, your plan of action should be pretty clear by now. Your first response is to escape. Under no circumstances should you attempt to stop or attack the intruder.

Most burglars are only after material possessions and want to avoid you as much as you should want to avoid them. Don't escalate the severity of their crime by challenging or trying to detain them. Out of an instinct to survive, many nonviolent burglars turn violent when cornered or trapped. Sometimes they commit other "crimes of opportunity," such as sexual assault, when "caught" by a homeowner.

As in each of my Ten Tips, just use common sense in developing your plan and take a few seconds to think about the prudent thing to do. Ninety-nine percent of the time, it is best to first back away from the fight and assess the enemy before engaging in combat.

WHAT TO DO IF ASSAULTED

You have done everything you possibly could to avoid becoming a victim of assault or — just the opposite — you have done nothing to avoid becoming a victim, and it finally happens: you become the target of an assailant. Now what?

YOUR GOAL — TO SURVIVE

First and foremost, your objective is to **survive** the assault. As I have stated, if all the assailant wants is material possessions, relinquish them quickly, without verbalizing or chastising, and distance yourself from him to avoid any further physical confrontation. If you are in an area with other people, the crime will probably last only seconds.

Don't escalate the severity of the situation by cursing or hesitating to obey his demands for your possessions. Even if you are an expressive or driven-type personality and always must get in the last word, plan to show restraint in your comments and actions. Many people have been severely injured or killed by assailants who later stated, in prison, that if the victim would have only done as told, nothing would have happened.

If your assailant wants to physically punish you, out of sexual or ethnic "revenge," then your objective must be to survive the attack with as little physical and psychological damage as possible. Often, the mental scars last as long, if not longer, as the physical scars.

SHOULD YOU SCREAM FOR
HELP WHEN ASSAULTED?

This is one of those controversial subjects for which there is no standard answer, and anyone who tells you to always scream "fire" or to never scream doesn't have the expertise he thinks he has. If you were to scream for help or at your assailant, one assailant might run and the next might just as quickly slit your throat.

There have been many interviews with convicted rapists and murderers on the effect of their victims' screams for help. Their comments are seldom the same. The outcome depends on the personality of the victim, the personality of the assailant and the circumstances of the attack.

When one convicted serial rapist/murderer was asked about the deciding factor in whether or not he killed his victims, he stated, "If they cooperated, I would release them after I [assaulted] them. If they fought or screamed, I would cut their throat, after [sexually assaulting] them." For this particular assailant, his criteria for deciding to kill or not was that simple.

Another convicted assailant said that screaming and fighting would prevent his attack. That is why it is so important to determine, in those first few seconds of an assault, what type of criminal and situation you are dealing with.

PREPARING YOUR
PLAN OF ACTION

It may be uncomfortable to think about being assaulted, but role-play a confrontation and develop a plan of action.

1. Give your assailant any material possessions requested.
2. Pay close attention to details — voice, mannerisms, physical features — but try to be aloof when doing so. Don't make it obvious, by staring, that you are storing as much

information about the individual as you can.

3. If you are isolated from other people and are with an angry or violent assailant, be prepared to physically defend yourself. If nothing else, raise your arms in front of you to ward off or accidently block blows, especially to the head.

4. If you are hesitant to counterattack and are struck by either a blow or weapon, it is probably best to feign unconsciousness or death. Very few assailants stay around long enough to punish a victim if they believe they have done sufficient damage.

5. If you decide to physically resist, attack your assailant's weak areas, which will be affected no matter the criminal's size or gender. Go for the eyes first, then the throat and groin areas. Use speed and surprise and immediately escape. Don't linger to see the results.

6. As soon as possible, relate a description of the assailant and the events to someone. You will remember more about the actual incident during the first few minutes after the assault than you will the next day. If there is no one to relate details to, write them down. If you have to, scratch them in the dirt with a stick or take a coin and scratch them on the sidewalk. Don't wait and try to remember the license number of a car the day after the assault. Many a criminal has been caught because his victim — even when fatally injured — scratched some vital information in the dirt.

7. Don't hesitate to seek professional help after an assault, no matter how minor the attack. The physical and emotional trauma of being victimized can be overwhelming. Police officers and military professionals can attest to the strain that physical violence can produce, not only on the victim but also their families, who must help the victim cope long after the actual assault.

8. Practice the awareness and avoidance concepts presented in this book and avoid suffering the experience of being victimized and having to cope with the aftereffects. If you do have to defend yourself, fight as though your life depends on it, because it probably does!

LOOKING FORWARD
TO BEING ATTACKED

Make sure you know who the enemy is before attacking. Sometimes even when you win the fight, you lose sight of the battle.

A woman had attended several self-defense courses and was just waiting for the chance to use her newly developed skills.   Her heightened sense of awareness had her on the razor's edge of readiness. She was determined that she would be intimidated no more by rude, crude, lecherous men.

She thought her chance had finally arrived one cold Saturday morning while she exited her automobile at a local shopping mall. As she closed and locked her car door, a man appeared from nowhere, approaching her rapidly between cars. Feeling uneasy, she decided to quickly distance herself from the suspicious-looking man. As she turned to head toward the mall entrance, she felt a tug on her overcoat and heard footsteps right behind her.

Immediately, she whirled and swung her purse as hard as she could, slamming it against the side of the bewildered man's head, knocking him down. She then followed up with the second part of the technique, the "verbal reinforcement," screaming at the top of her lungs, "Get out of here or I'll kill you!"

Caught totally off-guard, in extreme pain and thinking he had been accosted by some raving maniac just released from a mental institution, the man hurriedly retreated toward his car.

The woman, swelling with pride, turned to march into the mall to report the confrontation to the mall's security, when she suddenly felt another jerk on her coat. Spinning around, expecting to have to go back into action, she saw to her amazement there was no assailant to be found. It was then she realized that she had closed her car door snugly on the tail of her overcoat.

The next day she wrote a letter to the local paper, telling of her encounter and asking the paper to print the story, along with an apology to her unknown "victim."

6

Tip 6

If You Are Going to Carry a Weapon, Know How to Use It and Have It Available

---

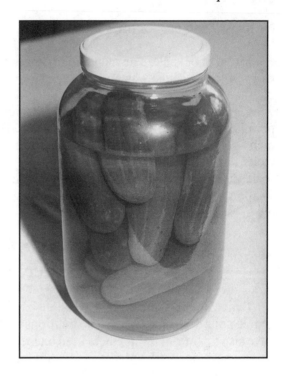

The most frequently asked question in all of my seminars is, "What is the best weapon to carry for self-protection?" There is only one weapon I can recommend that will always be effective for everyone. That weapon — the ultimate weapon — is a gallon jar of dill pickles.

Before a recent seminar, I was placing various weapons on a table for display, as I always do. In front of everyone, I placed an electronic stun gun, cans of chemical spray and pepper spray, a newspaper, a handgun, a knife, handcuffs, a police badge, a Kubotan, a car key, a highway flare, a telephone, about a dozen other weapons you have probably never seen or thought of, and of course the ultimate weapon, the gallon jar of dill pickles.

As I put the electronic stun gun on the table, a man in the audience asked what it was. After I briefly identified it, he said he was pleased to finally get to see one, since he had been thinking about buying two, one

for himself and one for his wife.

I was "shocked!" The man had no knowledge whatsoever about a weapon for which he was about to spend more than $200 for a pair.

Choosing and using a weapon for self-protection is by far the most popular subject in every seminar I present. That is probably because many people are looking for a quick fix for their fears as the number of violent assaults continues to rise. It is a sad state of affairs, but our society is reaching the point that possessing some type of self-protection weapon is going to be as necessary as it was in the frontier days of the old West.

KNOW THE ADVANTAGES AND DISADVANTAGES

I have not only used all the weapons presented in my seminars on people countless times in actual situations and training exercises, but have also intentionally had them used on me so that I could intelligently discuss each one's advantages, disadvantages and effectiveness.

I have sacrificed my own safety and sanity, as well as my associate's (sometimes they even volunteered), so that you would not have to wonder if the weapon would actually have the desired effect on an assailant.

Some people may think I'm a bit strange. But how else can you know, for instance, how effective an electronic stun gun or pepper spray is unless you experience the effects of the weapon? However, the only weapon I have been fortunate enough to avoid the physical effects of is a firearm. I have been shot at several times, and that is close enough for me.

Obviously I cannot review all the weapons available as self-protection tools, since that would encompass a book in itself, but I can outline for you some of the more common weapons on the market today and give you an almost objective viewpoint on their advantages and disadvantages. You will find that you may already possess some of the weapons, like the gallon jar of dill pickles, but were just unaware of their effectiveness.

YOUR PERSONALITY

No matter what weapon you choose as your "security blanket," it is of no use unless you are 100 percent sure your personality will allow you to use it. Whether your choice of a weapon is a martial art or a firearm, you must be certain you are mentally prepared to use it.

Many martial artists who have trained for years often freeze in a street confrontation because they have not been trained to be mentally prepared for a real situation. The only training many commercial martial arts schools offer is controlled sport karate, where sparring is done with pads and a referee controls the degree of seriousness. These students have never had to face being hit with bare fists and feet or a two-by-four. And the absence of a referee to break up a violent situation makes it very different than a training exercise.

Mental preparation in the use of a weapon is just as important as the ability to physically use the weapon of choice. When I ask my seminar participants who admit to carrying a firearm for protection if they are sure they could shoot someone if need be, many are unsure they could or would.

It is one thing to say or think that you would not hesitate to shoot someone, but it is a different situation when the real situation presents itself. As a former police officer, I can attest to the fact that on several occasions I had the legal right to use deadly force and chose not to. I was lucky several times and survived these incidents, but killing another human being is not as easy as it is portrayed in television police dramas.

Talk with any police officer and he or she will tell you the same thing. It is often found that the incident was not as deadly as first perceived, and the use of extreme or deadly force would have actually escalated the situation to a much more dangerous level than it actually was.

All assault situations do not warrant the use of deadly force. Take care in developing the attitude that if someone attempts to assault you with his fists, you have the right to pull out a gun and shoot him. You might quickly discover how much lawyers cost.

The victim of an assault has the same responsibilities as a police officer in the use of force against an assailant. That is, you may use only the force necessary to stop the attack. What would a reasonable person do in determining the justification for the use of force in self-defense?

ALWAYS REMEMBER THE "REASONABLE PERSON" RULE

That means that if someone runs by you and grabs your purse and is fleeing, you do not have the legal right to shoot or kill the thief. Legally, you may capture and detain that person by using reasonable force, but no more force is permissible if the assailant is not resisting.

Deadly force should not even be considered unless a person perceives the threat of serious bodily harm or death. That should always be your determining factor in deciding to use serious or deadly force against an assailant.

The interpretation of what reasonable force is varies greatly from state to state, which is all the more reason to outsmart your assailant rather than outfight or outgun him. For instance, in Texas some say that you can almost shoot first and then yell "halt" and be within your legal rights, but in New York, you may find yourself being sued or serving prison time for defending yourself against a known habitual criminal.

I know that sounds ridiculous and can be frustrating, but it is the law. You must be aware of your state and local statutes regarding the use of force or weapons to defend yourself. You must also be aware that each state has statutes governing when you can legally detain someone, and at what point it becomes "illegal detention," and when you might be liable for violating the criminal's "rights!" What you consider defending yourself might be interpreted by a court as assault.

Aggravated assault often implies the use of a weapon or a threat where serious bodily harm or death is either possible or threatened. When such circumstances exist, you then have the legal right to defend yourself using whatever force is necessary to stop the intended or actual

attack. The use of a firearm or other weapon would be justified in most such instances. However, since it is usually illegal to carry a firearm, if your weapon is illegally possessed you are still liable under the existing laws of the particular city or state.

I do not recommend carrying a firearm for protection. Innocent citizens put themselves in a position of being sued because the confrontation often could have been handled using a nonlethal self-protection weapon.

It is always best to avoid the situation and not have to make such a difficult and long-lasting decision. That is why it is so important to study the other tips in this book.

ONCE YOU HAVE
USED DEADLY FORCE

It can be, and often is, just as devastating for the person who kills or critically injures an assailant as for the victim of an attack.

Many criminals are now suing the person they attacked for using excessive force in self-defense. Quite often, the criminals are winning in court. You might be thinking that corpses don't file lawsuits — but their families do.

In talking with citizens and police officers who have had to take another person's life in defending themselves, I have discovered that they also suffer in many ways. Many people eventually end up moving from the home where they have had to shoot an intruder. The trauma and stress associated with such incidents are much greater than most people realize.

And once you have used deadly force to defend yourself, it becomes difficult to ever do it again. The second time, questions develop immediately, such as was it really "self-defense" again?

Many police officers are forced out of their profession after being involved in a controversial fatal shooting, even when it was found justified. Even when cleared of charges, an officer might hesitate in a

similar situation because of all the problems associated with a fatal shooting, thus endangering his life.

Many people have told me they carry a firearm for the security they feel from just having it with them.   That is understandable, but dangerous.   If you are not prepared to use your weapon of choice, it serves no purpose, except as a possible weapon for the assailant in the event he wrests it from you.   That happens much more often than people like to think.   Each year, statistics show that more people are killed with their own handguns than the total number of people who are shot and killed in self-defense (justifiable homicide).

My recommendations for the best self-protection weapons to use are based on comments and feedback from seminar participants. Many people attend my seminars solely because they are looking for an alternative weapon to a firearm.   Either they are afraid to use a firearm or afraid to have one in the home because they have children.   Many people, after seeing the various weapons, change their attitudes about them considerably.

I find that many people are afraid to use the stun gun for fear that they might shock themselves or would hesitate to shock someone else. If you have any doubt that you couldn't use the weapon you carry for protection, get yourself another weapon immediately.

Be sure you are confident in your choice of weapon.   Be prepared for the effects on you, your family, and the assailant's family, both mentally and physically, if you are forced to use that weapon.

YOU MUST HAVE THE WEAPON AVAILABLE WHEN NEEDED

I am still amazed at the number of people who carry various weapons for protection but never have them in their hand at the critical time.   That is the most common mistake people commit in relying on a weapon for protection. Many people base their security on just having the weapon nearby or on their person, as if the weapon is going to come to their aid independently when needed.

You are not going to have time to dig through your purse or glove box to find your firearm, pepper spray or stun gun when the need arises. For example, entering your home or approaching your vehicle after shopping are two critical times when you must have your weapon in your hand. If you have to search to find it, I can assure you that your assailant is not going to wait to give you the time.

KNOW THE EXPECTED RESULTS

As a part of every seminar I present on weapons, I allow one of the participants to "stun" me. When I handed a stun gun to the man I spoke of earlier in this chapter who wanted to purchase two of them, he was nervous about shocking me. He was even prepared to catch me as I fell to the ground from being stunned.

However, *he* was stunned after shocking me and seeing me only recoil with anger. Once educated to not only the advantages but the disadvantages of his choice of weapon, he realized that there is much more than inflated commercial claims to be considered before making such an important purchase. He prudently decided to postpone his purchase and do further research.

Most people have no idea of the expected results if they are forced to use their stun gun, chemical spray, pressure point training or whatever their chosen weapon.

YOU MUST KNOW HOW TO USE YOUR CHOSEN WEAPON

That critical element is ignored much too often and is the reason many assault victims and innocent bystanders are injured or killed. A common and often fatal mistake is that most people never practice with their weapon and often forget how to use it or that they even have it. I have talked with hundreds of men and women in self-defense seminars and some admit to carrying self-protection weapons. But when I ask how many have ever actually used the weapon, more than three-fourths have never even had any kind of formal training.

If you carry or own a weapon for self-protection, get some professional instruction in using it, if you haven't already. For example, if you buy a firearm for protection, the first thing you should do is call your local police department to arrange for some formal training. If the police do not offer classes, they can refer you to an officer within their ranks who is a Certified Firearms Instructor, who often conducts seminars as a side business. Sadly, most police officers have to hold down second jobs because of their ridiculous and undeservedly low salaries for such a dangerous job.

The business where you purchased your weapon is usually a good source for training references. And of course, DEFENSIVE LIVING™ INC. is an excellent source for training classes in the use of all the weapons discussed in this book.

PRACTICE AND
BECOME PROFICIENT

When faced with a real-life situation, many times a police officer, who constantly trains with his firearm and is required to qualify as a marksman monthly, will fire several shots that miss a human target. Sometimes they empty their guns and never hit what they aimed at.

Many martial arts "experts" who never train under realistic circumstances find out the hard way what little effect their sport techniques have in response to an assault by a violent or armed assailant. Whatever you choose for protection, it is imperative that you know how to use it and routinely practice realistically with it.

HAVE A BACKUP PLAN

No matter what weapon you choose, you should always have a backup plan in case the expected results fail to occur. That is not the time to start planning your backup course of action.

Your main objective should always be to avoid the situation. And if you can't avoid the situation, your objective should be to avoid injury and death and to escape.

WEAPONS FOR SELF-PROTECTION

FIREARM
(HANDGUN, RIFLES, SHOTGUNS)

Probably the most popular and well-known of all self-protection weapons is the firearm. When we speak of citizens arming themselves against criminals, we automatically think of some kind of gun. I am not going to discuss all of the controversial views regarding the right to bear arms for protection, though I will admit that I agree wholeheartedly with the right to defend my family and property with whatever means is necessary.

Anyone who comes from a rural state and grows up learning how to shoot has a big advantage over an adult trying to learn the basics of firearm safety for the first time. There are probably more firearms in my home state of Arkansas than in many nations' armies. Most firearms are used for sport and protection, but there are many important things to consider before deciding that a firearm is your answer as the ultimate weapon for self-protection.

The most important thing to consider is being certain you will use it if forced to protect yourself and your family.

ADVANTAGES

EFFECTIVENESS

As far as **physical effectiveness**, there is probably no equal. When the danger reaches the survival level, a firearm can become the determining factor in living or dying. A five-foot, one hundred-pound, ninety-year-old woman armed with the proper firearm and training can stop even the largest assailant — man or beast. Even when the actual firing of the firearm is not a choice, its **mental effectiveness** can be just as powerful.

As a police officer, I found it to be one of the easiest and most "humane" ways of quelling a potentially dangerous situation. I was in a near-riot situation with forty to fifty young gang members about to go on a rampage. One other officer and I responded and we knew there were no more units on the way to back us up. As the mood grew more hostile, I kicked a shell into the chamber of my 12-gauge riot shotgun. It's amazing what power the sound of "chambering" a shell has. That mental form of self-defense worked wonders. It looked as if I had just flushed a covey of quail in an Arkansas farm field. In a matter of seconds, the "covey" of gang members had flown the coop. Fortunately for my partner and me, that was all it took to neutralize the crisis that night.

For the person trained in the proper use of a firearm and using it strictly for home protection, the firearm is still one of the most effective choices for protection. However, I don't recommend a firearm as the first choice as a weapon for self-protection. Most people are often in as much danger from possessing a firearm as the potential assailant they are trying to protect themselves against.

DISADVANTAGES

CARRYING IT IS OFTEN ILLEGAL

If crime continues to rise at an epidemic rate, we all may have to revert to the frontier days of wearing a handgun on our hips just to survive. But currently, unless you are a police officer or have a permit to carry a firearm, you are breaking the law.

Most states have strict and definitive laws regarding the possession of a firearm in your home or while traveling in your vehicle. Care must be taken when traveling between states, because those laws vary greatly, as does the punishment for possession of a firearm.

Unless you have the weapon of choice in your hand when needed, its protection value is limited. Obviously, it is quite difficult and almost always illegal to walk in public with a firearm in your hand or strapped on your hip. If you are unsure, call the police to find out the laws on possession of firearms.

REPERCUSSIONS

Be aware of the repercussions of inflicting more injury than either intended or legally allowed. You as a law-abiding citizen have legal responsibilities to obey the law and use only the force necessary to stop the assailant's force.

DEADLY FORCE

A firearm's sole purpose is to inflict deadly force, but quite often the situation does not warrant that response. A crime such as purse-snatching does not legally warrant shooting the assailant.

If you accidentally kill a child who is committing a burglary or theft involving a few dollars, the legal, moral and emotional stress you might suffer will remain long after. As many private citizens and police officers have found, the legal implications of unjustified deadly force, whether intentional or not, is not taken lightly by the courts.

Relying on a firearm for all situations creates a greater degree of liability for the one defending himself than on the criminal.

FIREARMS ARE USUALLY
NOT FORGIVING

A man recently fatally shot his fifteen-year-old son as the boy crawled in through a bedroom window trying to avoid his father's wrath for breaking curfew. I can't even begin to comprehend what that father must be going through and will endure for the rest of his life.

Many innocent family members are often the victims of accidental

shootings and are even mistaken for a burglar or intruder. How many times have you read in the paper where a person shot someone to death and said he meant only to scare an attacker? Accidental deaths from firearms kill more people in some states some years than die in traffic accidents.

FIREARMS DEMAND EXTENSIVE TRAINING TO BE EFFECTIVE

Most people never develop the proficiency required to effectively and safely possess a firearm. It takes much longer than you think to pull a gun out and fire effectively. It is estimated that a police officer needs a twenty-two-foot space between himself and an assailant in order to draw his weapon and fire two shots before his attacker can reach him. And the officer still has to hope he hits him with one or both shots.

IF YOUR FIREARM IS TAKEN FROM YOU

When dropping off his wife and daughter at one of my seminars, a man came up to me and told me he didn't need my DEFENSIVE LIVING Tips at home because he keeps a loaded gun in every room and will kill any intruder.

I asked him, "What will you do when you arrive home someday and stumble into a prowler in your home who you helped arm to the teeth?" He didn't reply, but he did stay for the seminar.

If an assailant takes your firearm from you, *you* will be the one threatened with deadly force. Many people are injured or killed with their own gun, either by a person who has found the weapon in the home or car or has taken it away in a struggle. Even police officers, who practice gun retention techniques, often are disarmed and injured or killed. It is estimated that twenty-five to thirty-five percent of the police officers killed in the line of duty are fatally wounded with their own firearms. In fact, more police officers are killed with their own firearms than the number of people killed by police officers.

Many firearms end up being stolen from automobiles and homes of law-abiding citizens by criminals and used on other innocent people.

By using a less-than-lethal self-protection weapon, such as a pepper spray, you eliminate the chance of being fatally injured with your own weapon.

ESCALATION OF FORCE

The use of a firearm as a protection weapon often escalates the severity of the confrontation. Thirty percent to fifty percent of assaults and robberies are committed without the use of a weapon. Eighty percent of rapes are committed by assailants using only verbal threats and hands or fists as their weapons. Often, the firearm becomes a weapon of convenience for the assailant after disarming his victim in a confrontation.

COST

A firearm is one of the more expensive choices of weapons. Most reliable handguns cost from $100 to $200 and many are $500 and more. Rifles or shotguns fall in the same price range. If the firearm is stolen, the replacement cost is much higher than if it were a unit of pepper spray.

ELECTRONIC STUN GUNS

Stun guns are battery-powered devices that produce an electric shock, usually by touching the weapon's two probes to the assailant's body. They can be purchased in most law enforcement and gun supply stores. The cost varies from $50 to $150, depending on the amount of voltage produced and the quality of the device. Before investing in any weapon, always consult with local authorities to find out if the weapon can legally be carried in public. As with firearms, state and local restrictions may apply.

There are several myths that need to be addressed regarding stun guns.

Myth: Application and activation of a stun gun to an assailant will render him totally helpless and nearly unconscious.

I have been shocked dozens of times by stun guns and have yet to collapse into unconsciousness. That is not to say that I found it a

pleasant experience. Far from it. Depending on the assailant's sanity and his knowledge of stun guns, the effects can vary greatly. A shock from a stun gun might cause one assailant to attack much more aggressively, and the next might flee at just the sound and sight of a stun gun being activated. Unless a stun gun is held on a person at least three to five seconds, the assailant often only jerks away. What he does after that initial confrontation is anyone's guess. Speaking from experience, I have yet to meet the person who can hold me long enough to keep a stun gun applied to any part of my body for three seconds.

Myth: Stun guns are not safe to use if you've had heart problems, or they shouldn't be used on vital areas, such as the throat, groin or eyes.

A stun gun is considered a nonlethal weapon and thus is safe for use on — or by — someone with heart trouble without the fear of death because of electric shock. I usually hurt myself more by trying to escape the electric shock of a stun gun than from the shock itself.

As for the limitations on areas to attack, my philosophy is that anything is a target if you are being attacked or sexually abused. If the assailant injures himself trying to escape, that's his tough luck.

As with any weapon, if you have a stun gun or plan to purchase one, make sure you:

1. Buy one from a reputable dealer, such as a police equipment supply store or gun shop.
2. Have a friend lightly shock you with the gun on the hand or forearm to familiarize yourself with its effects.
3. Make sure you have it in your hand at those critical times when attacks are most frequent — which is when walking to and from your vehicle and entering and leaving your home.

ADVANTAGES

IT IS A NONLETHAL
SELF-PROTECTION WEAPON

Some assaults, robberies and sexual assaults do not legally warrant the use of deadly force. If an assailant is unarmed, using a firearm could result in your being held liable. From a liability standpoint, the

stun gun reduces your potential liability for using it to protect yourself.

If the assailant takes the stun gun away, he doesn't have the lethal capability he would have if you had been armed with a firearm.

PSYCHOLOGICAL EFFECT

Even if you have never experienced the shock of a stun gun, the weapon's physical appearance is enough to deter most unarmed assailants, especially when you discharge a short burst toward him. In many cases, that in itself is enough to discourage an assailant.

I've been shocked many times, but I must admit I never look forward to the next seminar when it's my turn to be on the receiving end. Many correctional institutions are using electronic stun devices to quell disruptive prisoners and have found them effective in neutralizing would-be troublemakers. A shield with multiple (twelve to twenty) electronic probes is used to remove disruptive prisoners, and usually just the sight of this device is enough to make them comply. The thought of fifteen to twenty stun gun probes hitting me at one time would make me become agreeable.

IS EASY TO CARRY AND CONCEAL

It's small, lightweight and easily carried in a purse or on your belt, where it should be when not in your hand. Most come with a convenient belt clip and resemble a pager or beeper. For walkers and runners, it is a good choice because it can be worn on a belt or even carried in your hand without being noticeable. You might sleep more restfully with a stun gun under your pillow than your .357-caliber magnum handgun. Most people are at least a little uncomfortable with a handgun under their pillow. I sure would be.

You can carry a stun gun in more places than a firearm. A firearm is not only often illegal, but it is rather difficult to walk or jog with one in your hand. A stun gun is legal and much more portable.

EFFECTIVE AGAINST ANIMALS

A short burst from a stun gun will usually send a threatening dog or animal retreating, especially one that has had previous experience

with electric fences. They tend to respect the stun gun much more than other weapons.

COST

Depending on your idea of expensive, the cost for most stun guns ranges from $40 to $130. If stolen or lost, the replacement cost is not as prohibitive as with a firearm.

OTHER PRACTICAL USES
FOR A STUN GUN

Recently, several medical research studies have documented cases where a stun gun was used to neutralize the damaging effect of venom on a person bitten by snakes or stung by poisonous insects. Many quail hunters use them to treat rattlesnake bites on their dogs. The dogs then continue hunting and usually show no effects from the bite.

It appears that the voltage from the stun gun, when applied immediately and directly to the affected area, breaks down the protein in the venom, thus neutralizing much of the damage. Future research bears watching, since this could make a stun gun a valuable weapon in a much different way for those out camping or hiking.

Finally, a stun gun is worth the price alone for waking your teenagers on school mornings after you have yelled at them at least a dozen times to get up. Just kidding, just kidding.

DISADVANTAGES

CLOSE CONTACT WITH THE
ASSAILANT IS REQUIRED

The stun gun is obviously much more effective when actual contact with the assailant is made. For the assailant to realize the complete effect, you must get close enough to apply the probes to the body. Close to the assailant is usually the last place you want to be. If you are surprised and attacked from behind, since you have no choice but to be in close contact with the assailant, a stun gun, if in your hand, could prove effective if applied to certain vital areas of the body. I'm sure you can think of a few.

CONTACT WITH BOTH
PROBES IS REQUIRED

That means you must be close to your assailant and within reach. That requires some precision in your application. Common sense should tell you that an assailant is not going to stand there and let you shock him.

If the assailant has warning that you are armed with a stun gun, he will be much more difficult to disable than an assailant you surprise. There is no way to be certain whether you should expose the stun gun and emit a burst of electricity to intimidate the assailant into retreat, or use the element of surprise and wait until you are close enough to attempt to shock the assailant.

With proper training on how to maintain control of the weapon, threatening with a short burst of the gun can be a useful move. If you are surprised and immediately come into contact with an assailant, then obviously you don't want to warn him with a burst of the gun, unless it happens to be between his legs. That is how to warn your attacker!

THE EFFECTS ARE NOT
ALWAYS PREDICTABLE

Some people are not affected by the gun's electric charge. Depending on the physical makeup of the person, his mental condition and his previous exposure to electric shock, the effects can be less than expected.

I have one staff member who, when shocked with a stun gun, doesn't even recoil. Each person, when shocked, appears to react differently and experiences different levels of discomfort and pain. I have shocked several electricians and people who work around electrical equipment who have been shocked many times previously, and the effect on them is minimal. Someone on drugs or alcohol would not be affected as greatly, since their pain threshold is much higher because of the drug's numbing effect on the nerves.

LEGALITIES

In some states, electronic protection devices are illegal. Check with local and state authorities. Few if any airlines permit the possession of

a stun gun and the state you arrive in may prohibit their possession, so be sure to check with the authorities in the state you plan to visit before taking one with you on vacation or a trip.

A stun gun is a useful alternative as a self-protection weapon. As with any weapon, you must have it available and be trained in the proper use of it. Your purse, glove box or dresser is not the place for it. Have it in your hand or on your belt when approaching those dangerous situations. And don't forget to put a battery in it.

AEROSOL PROTECTION DEVICES AND CHEMICAL REPELLENTS

I believe a repellent spray is one of the best self-protection weapons you can own, but it must be the right one. If you decide that a spray device is just what you are looking for, there are a few things you need to know. The most important is that all sprays are not alike. Advertising claims fail to point out major differences in self-protection sprays.

OLEORESIN CAPSICUM (OC) PEPPER SPRAY

It is often said that to be an excellent salesperson, you must first believe in the product you are selling. If that is the case, then I could make a fortune selling OC, or pepper spray as I affectionately call it. I am a 7th Degree black belt in karate and jujitsu and have trained in the martial arts for thirty years. If I had to defend myself against an assailant tomorrow, I would without hesitation use my pepper spray before using my martial arts skill. It is that effective.

WHAT IS OC OR PEPPER SPRAY?

Pepper spray is just what the name implies. It is a self-protection spray that uses the extracts of the common red pepper found in many gardens. It is an organically based, less-than-lethal spray repellent.

However, not all pepper sprays are the same, nor are the delivery systems. For the sprays I recommend, the delivery system is a cone-

shaped spray mist similar to hair spray, with a visible range of several feet. The effective range is usually six to eight feet. As the propellent evaporates, the active agent, pepper, continues to drift in the air, invisible but still effective.

Unlike tear gasses, which are classified as irritants, pepper sprays act as an inflammatory. A one-second burst in the face will dilate the capillaries of the eyes, causing instant but short-term blindness. In most cases, it induces immediate coughing and choking. The mucous membranes may swell to prevent all but life-support breathing, thus preventing further aggressive activity.

The effects of pepper spray normally last thirty to forty minutes. Because of the disorientation due to temporary blindness and the intense burning of the affected area, the person sprayed often loses his balance and puts his hands to his face or sits on the ground. Sounds wonderful, doesn't it?

There are many reasons that I recommend such a spray over other weapons. When you consider all of the many advantages and the few disadvantages of using pepper spray, I'm sure that you will understand why it is such a good choice.

ADVANTAGES

IT IS LESS-THAN-LETHAL

In the majority of confrontations, on the street and in family disturbances, a lethal or deadly response is often neither legal nor justified. Unlike a firearm, pepper spray is "forgiving" if used inappropriately, since there are no physical injuries or lasting effects from its use. Defending yourself with pepper spray greatly reduces your liability, compared to defending yourself using a firearm. And you can't accidentally kill a family member or innocent bystander with pepper spray.

A police officer attempted to shoot a pit bull terrier that was attacking a small child. The dog was on top of the child when the officer arrived and the father was standing over the dog, attempting to

beat it away. The officer fired his service weapon at the dog in an attempt to save the child. He missed the dog but hit the father, killing him instantly. Had he had pepper spray available, he could have neutralized the dog immediately, causing only temporary discomfort to both the child and father.

IT'S EFFECTIVE

Extensive tests and field use by the FBI, thousands of police departments and prisons confirm the outstanding results of pepper spray as a humane method of controlling an attacking or unruly person.

Since pepper spray is an inflammatory agent, you cannot build up an immunity to its effects. If an assailant is on drugs or drunk, the effects of pepper spray are just as formidable. That is an important advantage, since many other forms of self-protection have little or no effect on an assailant who is high on cocaine, for instance.

Since the affected areas are the eyes and respiratory system, the size of the assailant is unimportant. I have sprayed hundreds of police officers of all sizes, and many were certain they couldn't be neutralized with pepper spray. The score so far: Pepper spray 100 percent, police officers 0 percent.

Its effectiveness without the use of physical force is a distinct advantage compared to other self-protection weapons such as martial arts, pressure point tactics, active resistance methods and stun guns. It is most potent at six to eight feet from an assailant and some units are effective from as far away as twenty feet. Even when you are surprised from behind, a short burst of pepper spray over your shoulder will incapacitate an assailant, something few weapons can claim to do.

Most self-protection weapons guarantee no extended time to escape. The effects of pepper spray last long enough (twenty to forty-five minutes) to allow you ample time to escape — and remember, that is your primary goal. You will even have time to call the police and tell them where the assailant is, because he won't be able to see to escape for about twenty to thirty minutes at the minimum.

IT TAKES LITTLE TRAINING TO
BECOME AND STAY PROFICIENT

Another important advantage of pepper spray as a self-protection weapon is that it requires little training to be extremely effective. Unlike firearms, martial arts and other commercial self-defense programs, one can become realistically proficient with pepper spray in a two-hour seminar. No other self-protection weapon can claim a proficiency level with as little training. Even the ultimate weapon, a gallon jar of dill pickles, takes a little more training time.

IT IS EXCELLENT AGAINST
MULTIPLE ASSAILANTS

Make sure the spray is dispersed in a cone-shaped mist, not a stream. It is effective against more than one person, unlike stun guns, pressure point tactics and martial arts techniques. The cone-shaped pattern increases the probability of an assailant accidentally passing through the spray, even when you have nervously missed your target.

Defending oneself at night is difficult enough without having to worry about whether you can hit the assailant with tear gas, which shoots in a stream, or a firearm. For a police officer, that is a distinct advantage, since many officers hesitate to shoot at an assailant at night because of the liability from injuring an unarmed person.

It is very difficult to determine in a split second if a suspicious-acting person is holding a gun or a cigarette lighter. If you spray the subject with pepper spray, only to find out he was holding a lighter, you still have a job. If you shoot him with a firearm, you could very well be working as a security guard at a wrecking yard the next week.

DOES NOT REQUIRE
YOU TO COME IN CONTACT
WITH THE ASSAILANT

For smaller people, it is an excellent equalizer. Police officers who are not large and intimidating are often at a physical disadvantage when dealing with multiple assailants. Pepper spray can even the odds easily. Female officers, when faced with much larger male subjects, can easily control them with pepper spray.

Pepper spray is an excellent self-protection weapon for the elderly and physically handicapped. Most units come in a case with a belt clip, and the entire unit (case and spray) is removed from the belt when used. There is no need to remove it from the case, whether carried on your belt or in your hand, to activate it.

PORTABLE AND EASY
TO CONCEAL

The units are small and can fit in the palm of your hand. Pepper spray is excellent to carry when walking or jogging because of its small size and light weight. It produces excellent results on animals. It has been proven effective on attack dogs, cats and even sharks and grizzly bears. I once had cats getting in my trash at all hours of the night. Now, I periodically spray my trash cans, and guess what? No cats in the trash anymore.

LEGALITIES

Pepper spray is legal to possess in most states. It is still wise to check with local authorities before purchasing. And, as with any weapon, proper training in the use of pepper spray is highly recommended. Pepper spray, like many other weapons, is prohibited on any airline. The penalties are severe and strictly enforced, so be sure not to accidentally carry any even in your luggage. You wouldn't want your spray unit to burst and fill the airplane with pepper gas, especially the cockpit.

You are responsible for exercising reasonable care in the use of any weapon, including pepper spray. You can be charged with assault if you use any weapon without justification. Likewise, if you do have to use pepper spray on an assailant, you should ensure that the assailant doesn't accidentally wander in front of a moving car, since he will be blind for about thirty minutes.

Always make sure that you immediately report any attempted assault to the police. There is nothing to keep the assailant you have sprayed from reporting *you* as the assailant. This happens rarely, but it has occurred.

COST

It is one of the best buys, costing from $10 to $20, depending on the size. You can get a unit that contains about ninety one-second bursts. If you need more than that, you need to find another neighborhood or get another job. If lost or stolen, the replacement cost is minimal.

DISADVANTAGES

THE BLOW-BACK EFFECT

If forced to use pepper spray outdoors, be aware of possible blow-back of the spray. If there is a wind blowing, it is important to continue to move away from the assailant to ensure that you are not contaminated by the spray. But once you use your weapon, no matter what weapon it is, escape as soon as possible and notify authorities.

Indoors, the effects of the spray on yourself should be minimal if used correctly. That is why it is so important to receive proper training in the use of pepper spray. You should always use one-second bursts against an assailant to prevent contamination of others, especially yourself.

ALL PEPPER SPRAYS
ARE NOT THE SAME

The percentage of pepper in the sprays varies. I have seen some with as little as .01 percent (one one-hundredth of 1 percent). I even sprayed it directly on my tongue and experienced very little effect. Make sure there is at least 1 percent of OC in the spray. Having had 1 percent and 5 percent solutions in my eyes, nose and lungs many times, the effects were such that I do not plan to spray a 1 percent, or greater, solution on my tongue any time soon.

The size of the canister is also important. Some of the smaller units do not have enough range (less than two feet) to keep your assailant at a distance, and they dispense very little spray. Test fire (outdoors) any unit you have purchased to make sure it sprays and to find out its range. Attempting to stop an assailant charging at you is not the time to discover that you have a defective unit. Make sure whatever brand you purchase is certified by one of the larger manufacturers.

Also be aware that the agent that creates the spray and carries the pepper varies. The most effective I have found are those that use alcohol. It evaporates rapidly, and the pepper is not effective until the agent evaporates. Some sprays use chemicals and other agents that create a stream, rather than the cone-shaped mist. They require much better aim and usually take valuable time in causing any effect.

And even others use deadly gases, such as freon and halon. I would hate to cause permanent injury to someone I mistakenly believed was an assailant or to myself in the event of a blow-back, as described earlier, or if the spray is used against me.

MOST PEOPLE DON'T
RECEIVE CERTIFIED TRAINING

Since pepper spray is so effective, many people assume they don't need any training. As with any weapon, you must go through some realistic training if you are to know the expected results, know how to use it and have practiced and become proficient with it. A properly taught two-hour course is the minimum training I recommend.

Considering all factors, I find pepper spray one of the best self-protection weapons for anyone. Not only for citizens, but for police officers, because it is an effective but humane method of temporarily disabling an assailant.

It is affordable for anyone. For the executive, runner, housewife or the parent worried about a young adult at college, it is such a practical choice that it is wise to have several. For the elderly and physically handicapped, it should be *the* choice for a self-protection weapon.

Having one in the home and one in the car at all times for emergencies is affordable. As with any weapon, though, treat it as such. Stun guns, firearms and pepper sprays are not to be used except when a clear and present danger exists. They are not toys. Any abuse of a weapon only furthers the prohibition of that weapon.

I have certified hundreds of police officers and citizens in the use of pepper spray. After being exposed to pepper spray, all agree that it is one of the best self-protection weapons available.

CHEMICAL REPELLENTS

Tear gas (CN/CS) is one of the best known self-protection spray repellents. It is a less-than-lethal weapon and at one time was one of the most popular weapons for citizens and police alike when a firearm was not practical or legal. The effects of chemical repellents can be varied, and there are several important factors to consider before choosing a tear gas spray.

Although CN/CS repellents have some positive attributes compared to many forms of nonlethal weapons, the pepper spray devices that I have discussed in this chapter have many more advantages.

DISADVANTAGES

EFFECTIVENESS

Many people are not affected by chemical repellents. In many cases, intoxicated, drugged, enraged or demented people have reduced sensitivity to pain. Tear gas products are irritants that cause discomfort or a burning sensation of the skin and certain body areas when sprayed.

CN/CS or tear gas sprays depend on the pain process to be effective, and when an assailant is high on drugs or alcohol, tear gas sprays have little or no effect. Many criminals have been sprayed by police officers so many times that they frequently build up an immunity to the effects. I have sprayed several people with tear gas sprays when arresting them, and the only effect it had on some was to make them laugh.

Many animals are not affected by tear gas sprays because they lack tear ducts. Police and animal control officers have learned the hard way that some attack dogs are not affected by such sprays.

DELAYED RESULTS EVEN WHEN EFFECTIVE

Even when effective, often fifteen to thirty seconds pass before the chemical irritant begins to work. An assailant can do severe damage in that amount of time. Compounding that problem is not knowing in that fifteen to thirty seconds if the spray is even going to have an effect. Thirty seconds into an assault is not the time to find out that the assailant is not the least bit affected by your tear gas.

TEAR GAS SPRAYS SHOOT A SINGLE STREAM

Rather than a cone-shaped mist, most tear gas products shoot a stream of chemical and you can often miss your target. It can be difficult, especially at night, to hit the intended target — the chest area — with a single stream. The fact that the assailant is not going to stand perfectly still for you and the stress you will be under when assaulted both make relying on this kind of spray questionable.

OTHER WEAPONS

There are other alternative weapons I have mentioned in this chapter, like the gallon jar of dill pickles. The nice thing about the following items is that their primary use is not intended to be a weapon. Always remember, there are ingenious ways to get around technicalities and particular wordings of laws.

Let's briefly define what a weapon is. A weapon is not always defined by the object itself, but rather its use. For example, if I were to pick up a spoon and attack you with it, then obviously that spoon has become a weapon. There are two important points to remember about this concept. First, anything can be considered a weapon if the intent of the person using it is to use it as a weapon. Second, many objects can be carried legally on your person or in your vehicle, without being considered weapons.

Even a firearm, in some states, is perfectly legal to carry in a vehicle if it is in the trunk of your car. The logic is that obviously a firearm is not readily accessible as a weapon if it is locked in the trunk.

Depending on your state and local laws, even this example may be illegal. But in many rural states, farmers year-round have their rifles and shotguns openly displayed in gun racks in their trucks. They have a legitimate need and often have to kill snakes and predators on their farms. So depending on the area of the country you live in, what is classified as a weapon and what is classified illegal possession of a weapon can vary greatly.

ITEMS THAT CAN BECOME WEAPONS IN AN EMERGENCY

RAILROAD OR HIGHWAY FLARES

I grew up playing with railroad flares. My father was a switchman for the Cotton Belt-Railroad, so the railroad flare was one of his tools of trade. He taught me that the flare could be used to get attention if we had car problems. But he also taught me to see the other uses in various tools and how you can find other ways to use an item. I can remember him using the flares to build a fire and how easy they made starting a fire when the wood was damp. My father taught our family to keep several of the flares in our car for emergencies. Of course, back then, he wasn't referring to the same kind of emergencies we face today in our crime-ridden society.

The highway flare is nothing more than a large match (approximately ten inches long) that, when ignited, is used to warn approaching motorists that a hazardous road condition exists. They are not used as frequently as in the past because reflective markers have become the predominant choice today of police agencies and trucking firms.

The highway flare becomes an excellent self-protection weapon in an emergency. It encompasses the best of two good self-protection weapons. The flare, once ignited, becomes a weapon comparable to a stun gun and spray repellent. It shoots a three-inch to five-inch flame that is intimidating. After burning for a few seconds, it begins to drip a hot molten liquid, which when flicked toward an assailant's eyes will keep even the most daring assailant away.

The flare will usually last for ten to fifteen minutes, long enough to provide ample time to escape. It is an excellent item to keep in the car or home for several reasons:

1. It is not a weapon and is perfectly legal to carry in your vehicle.
2. It is small and easy to carry if you were to break down on the highway and had to walk for help.
3. It can keep several assailants at bay when swung back and

forth in front of you because of the molten liquid it produces.

4. It is an inexpensive weapon. Most flares cost between $1.50 to $2.50 each. The best price I have seen is $1.19 each. They can be purchased at most automotive supply stores. Be sure to buy several and practice striking and lighting them before the need arises. Always strike away from your body so you don't accidentally burn yourself. They can be quickly extinguished by sticking the flaming end into the ground.

5. If necessary, a flare can be used to start a fire to gain attention. When one woman with car trouble was approached by an assailant, she fled into the nearby woods and used a flare to set the woods on fire. Every volunteer fire fighter within fifty miles was there within five minutes and the potential assailant was nowhere to be found.

6. It is an excellent deterrent to carry with you if you walk or run and are bothered by dogs. Even a pit bull terrier has respect for fire.

In my seminars, I recommend keeping a flare under the driver's and passenger's seats. Many rapists, when abducting a victim, force the victim to lie on the floorboard of the passenger side. What a wonderful surprise it would be to come up from the floorboard with the flare ignited and directed at his legs or other areas. You might burn a few holes in your car seats with the dripping liquid, but consider the alternative.

HOME OR CAR KEY

One of the most useful items to consider as a self-protection tool is a key. At first you might not think of your key as being large enough to serve any protective purpose, but it is one of the best for many reasons.

IT IS VERY AVAILABLE

One of the most common times for attacks is when you are either entering your auto or home. The assailant often uses the auto or home as a cover for his intended crime. If he can attack you just as you are entering your car, he can use it as a means to escape, with you inside.

By attacking as you open the door to your house or apartment and forcing you inside, he uses your home as an aid in completing the crime. Remember from Tip 2; don't go in your home with an intruder. After Tip 9, you will know what to do.

You normally have your key in your hand when entering or exiting your home or car, so it is usually the most accessible item you have to defend yourself with. The number one reason to consider your key as a weapon is that it is usually the most available tool.

EFFECTIVENESS

A key held in the proper position can cause severe and devastating damage to an assailant. By holding your key under your forefinger with just the tip of the key protruding, as shown in pictures on this page, you can use it to strike sensitive areas such as the eyes, forehead, chest and back of the hand.

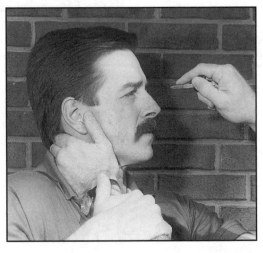

The proper position for the keys should be as described above, and not interlaced between the fingers, as many self-defense books describe. Rather than a raking motion with the keys, a stabbing and slashing motion is much more effective.

The back of the key should rest against the

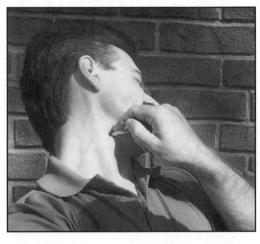

upper palm of your hand. That position reinforces the key from the rear while the thumb and second finger reinforce from the sides. This pecking or striking position is a natural position to use, even when you are not expecting to use the key as a weapon. It is an easy grip to develop and allows easy access to unlock your door, unlike the interlacing method.

IT MAKES AN IMPRESSION

The effectiveness of this method is easy to verify. Place your home or auto key in the position described and tap yourself lightly in the middle of your forehead. Tap harder and you will see exactly what I mean when I say it is effective. Now tap yourself in the upper chest area. You will notice the same effect. Imagine this applied to one of an assailant's eyes. Even attacking the forehead or chest with a medium amount of force will cause immediate, severe pain or damage. If someone grabs you, a strike with the key to the back of the hand several times will have immediate results. Try this on yourself.

To further appreciate the effectiveness of this weapon, take the key and press it to your neck, just to the side of your windpipe. Just imagine if you really thrust the key with force. Finally, take your key and strike an object such as a phone book or a piece of fruit and see the results.

MARKING YOUR ASSAILANT

The slashing effect after striking can serve to identify your assailant if he escapes and is apprehended later. A car key can tear skin and cut much like a knife.

IT IS NOT PERCEIVED AS A WEAPON

The wonderful thing about a key is that it can be carried with you at all times and not be considered a weapon. Now if you were to file the end to a razor sharp-point, I don't think it would be looked upon favorably in court, so don't go that far. It is really not necessary. Your key is all you need when properly used.

It is an excellent item for children to learn to use as a defensive weapon. A woman in one of my seminars recently asked about a

weapon for her thirteen-year-old daughter. The girl rides a school bus, and the walk between the bus stop each morning and afternoon and her home has become increasingly dangerous. Several abductions have occurred nearby. The mother pointed out that they live in a rural area and there aren't any homes nearby that her daughter could run to if confronted.

My first suggestion was to give her a key and teach her the proper way to use it as a weapon. Second, she could possibly leave an aerosol repellent, such as pepper spray, near the bus stop and walk with it to and from the bus stop each day. It's sad that we have to develop strategies to walk to and from a school bus stop, but in today's environment it has become a fact of life and a necessity to continue living.

It is important that you understand I am not endorsing ways to severely injure or maim people. I am only trying to help people deal with the fact that our society has changed dramatically in the last ten to fifteen years and nowhere can it be assumed that one is safe from the possibility of assault or attack. You must find ways to deal with this menace and use all means necessary to keep crime from adversely affecting your life.

A BELT

That's right, a belt. One with a nice heavy buckle. It's perfectly legal to wear anytime, anywhere, and you can even keep an extra one in your car in case your forget to put yours on in the morning.

In an emergency against even an armed assailant (excluding a firearm), the belt can become a formidable weapon for self-protection. In my seminars, I teach how to quickly remove your belt and wrap the end without the buckle around your hand a couple of times. This leaves an eighteen-inch to twenty-four-inch length of belt with a buckle on the end that, when swung like a helicopter blade over your head, can literally cut up an assailant in a matter of seconds.

Martial artists trained in the use of nunchaku fighting sticks can use the same maneuvers with a belt and often have even greater defensive capabilities. I assure you that if someone pulled a knife on me and I had a belt on, I wouldn't rely on my martial arts skills of kicking and

punching. I would rely instead on my skills of using my head and would remove my belt to slice them up like a loaf of bread.

MARTIAL ARTS

The martial arts include karate, judo and taekwondo. And what about all of us thousands of black belts with our martial arts skills? Is this not the ultimate reason to train in the martial arts, to become a "walking weapon?"

I have been involved in the martial arts since 1963 and it is truly a major part of my life. I have been fortunate enough to train with some of the leading experts in karate, judo and taekwondo. Fifteen to twenty years ago, I could honestly say that if an assailant unknowingly chose a Black Belt in the martial arts as a victim, he was in for a very bad day.

But because of the proliferation of commercial martial arts schools since the Vietnam War era, I must admit that many Black Belts today wouldn't have a chance on the streets. I don't say that out of resentment for what has happened to the martial arts. I speak from experience and talking with many thousands of Black Belts over the years.

Some systems promote people to Black Belt in two years, but that doesn't give them the knowledge and experience to walk confidently on the streets today. I talk every week to Black Belts who have received their rank from commercial "belt factories," and they are the ones who doubt their abilities. They aren't sure what they will do in a real street confrontation or if they even have the skill to survive one.

There are still a few traditional martial arts schools that offer realistic self-defense training. But the progress and rank advancement will be slow and effective. Yes, martial arts training can be an excellent choice as a self-protection weapon, but one must be selective in choosing a school.

ADVANTAGES

1. When properly trained, you always have your weapon with you. You *are* the weapon.
2. When properly trained, you can vary the degree of force

used against your assailant. If deadly force is justified, you have the capability to inflict it. If a lesser degree of force is justified, a properly trained person can deliver the correct amount of force to neutralize an assailant.

3. It is not only a practical method of self-defense, but is also beneficial to your overall cardiovascular conditioning and aids you mentally and physically.
4. It is an excellent form of exercise for children if the emphasis on rank and sport karate are de-emphasized.

DISADVANTAGES

1. It can give you false self-confidence in your actual ability to defend yourself in a real-life situation.
2. It can be difficult to find instruction in traditional martial arts (for the street).
3. The cost can be expensive, from $40 to $75 a month. Many schools require lengthy contracts.
4. It takes a minimum of four to six years to become proficient enough to handle a majority of assault situations (armed and unarmed). Most people never train long enough to reach that level of expertise. I have trained thirty years and finally have learned enough to know how much I still don't know.

OTHER MARTIAL ARTS PROGRAMS

ACTIVE RESISTANCE CLASSES

PRESSURE POINT SEMINARS

Several martial arts organizations offer pressure point seminars that purportedly teach non-martial artists basic skills in the art of defending oneself by attacking an assailant's pressure points. To imply that one can learn any form of self-defense in one to two hours is almost a form of negligence.

The last thing you want to do is prolong contact with an assailant. Grappling for pressure points and applying pressure to subdue an assailant is not only difficult, but dangerous. Your first goal is to

escape with little or no contact with the assailant.

These courses cost between $30 and $50 for two to three hours and offer few, if any, self-defense concepts for a novice learning street self-defense. It takes years of continuous practice to enable one to effectively strike or apply such physical techniques. It would be like taking a one-hour course in the use of a firearm and expecting to be proficient afterward. It takes years of practice when shooting only at targets before one is competent with a firearm. Include the stress and unpredictability of an actual assault, even when one is an expert, and the outcome is far from predictable.

Such pressure point courses should be limited to police and correctional officers who daily have to control prisoners.

KUBOTAN/YAWARA STICK TRAINING

Along with pressure point attack classes, Kubotan or yawara stick training is being offered by many martial arts schools. A Kubotan is a four-inch to six-inch stick, and often is part of a key chain. The Kubotan is a restraint device used for years by Japanese police departments. It is used to strike sensitive areas of the body. Since most Japanese police agencies do not permit the use of firearms, tools such as the Kubotan provide a humane, but effective method of controlling a prisoner or assailant.

Recently, classes on the use of the Kubotan have developed as self-defense classes have increased in popularity. You have to be wary of quick-fix classes that imply expertise in any form of self-protection is possible after only a few hours of training. Like any program that deals with physical techniques, it takes much more time to develop and understand intricate techniques. Constant reinforcement in the use of an object such as a Kubotan is necessary, and little, if any, is ever offered as a follow-up program.

The practicality of using a Kubotan for anyone other than law enforcement personnel is highly questionable, and compared to pepper spray, it is a waste of time and money.

1. Your goal is not to control the assailant, but to escape from him.
2. The striking effectiveness of the Kubotan can be duplicated

by using your middle knuckle, and you always have your middle knuckle with you.

3. If the use of the Kubotan is not reinforced periodically, it is of little or no value as a weapon.

You should be wary about one-time courses regardless of the claims made about the effectiveness of the weapon. The weapon is only as effective as the person behind it.

TECHNOLOGY WEAPONS

THE TELEPHONE

There are other forms of weapons that do not necessarily create physical damage but do cause mental damage.

The advent of cellular phone technology has probably done more to decrease the figures for assaults and harassment of motorists than anyone could have imagined. Holding a phone up to your ear when in your car and calling 911 when being harassed by some motorist is just as effective as waving a shotgun or pistol at him. And the former is much more legal.

Everyone should invest in a cellular telephone for his automobile as an excellent method of assault prevention. So many assaults, rapes and abductions are completed simply because the victim had no way to call for assistance. And how many thousands have been victims of murder, robbery and rape because they were forced to leave their disabled vehicle and search for a phone or assistance? You can pick up a newspaper any day and read of a crime of opportunity committed against a stranded motorist.

As the prices continue to fall, a cellular telephone will become economically available to most people. It should be considered a must for you or your teenagers. The transportable cellular phone can be plugged into a cigarette lighter when necessary.

TELEPHONE CUSTOM CALLING FEATURES

For the person plagued with obscene or annoying phone calls, there are several options available from your telephone company.

Caller ID

Already available in some states is the service that displays the caller's telephone number on your phone. It is known by several marketing names, but caller ID is the generic name for this service. The service allows the person receiving the call to view, via a phone with a display window, the telephone number he is being called from. The feature gives the person control over what call he wants to answer and identifies the telephone number of the calling party. It should all but eliminate the obscene phone call.

There is still some debate regarding privacy violations, but the benefits far outweigh any accidental identification. Soon, telephone harassment crimes will be extinct.

Voice Mail and Telephone Answering Machines

Voice mail, which is provided by some telephone companies and other vendors, or a telephone answering device can be used to deter obscene phone callers and trick possible intruders. Obscene phone callers are hesitant to leave a message. Recording their voice would obviously aid in their identification, and besides, some perverts are discouraged when they do not get to talk to a real person. Leaving a sick message on a recorder is just not the same.

Voice mail or an answering device can also be used to trick or confuse a potential burglar. My answering machine has this message: "Hello, this is Bo Hardy, I'm either on my other line or away from the phone for just a few minutes, so your call has been forwarded to my voice mail box. If you will leave your name and number, I will return your call as soon as possible."

Of course, my calls aren't really forwarded to a voice mail box, because it isn't available yet in my city, but no one else knows that. Stating that I might be on my other line leaves a potential criminal wondering whether I am home or not. Just because my phone was answered by an answering device does not automatically mean I am not home.

If you happen to be a single female, get a male friend to record your

message for you. Try to find one who sounds like he stands six-feet-eleven and weighs 350 pounds. And if you want to really send a signal, record a large dog barking in the background.

Call Forwarding

If you want to really have fun at the expense of an obscene or annoying caller, install call forwarding. The first time some pervert phones at 3:00 a.m., immediately forward your calls to the local police station. That should stop his calls. (You really should not forward the call to the police station, but it sure is a good thought.)

Plan a course of action, and ask a male neighbor or co-worker if you can forward him your calls if you have an obscene caller. After the first obscene call, call your friend, explain what has happened, and forward your calls to him. The next obscene call will be answered by a male, and there is no way the caller can know he is not there with you. This is yet another way to use the buddy system from Tip Number 3.

When away from your home for extended periods or just during the day, forward your calls to a friend who is home. If a burglar is attempting to find an unoccupied home, yours will not qualify. Our buddy in this instance is our telephone. This is much more effective than using an answering machine while on vacation. If a potential burglar engages an answering machine for several days, the chances that you are gone for an extended period are fairly certain.

Three-Way Calling

This feature is yet another service offered by many local telephone companies. Using it, you could have some fun at the expense of an obscene phone caller.

For example, the next time your obscene caller calls and starts to tell you all the things he is going to do to you, tell him to hold just a minute while you go put on something a little sexier. With three-way calling, you add on the police department, tell them what is going on and then bring Mr. Sicko back on.

By now, he is so ready to tell you all the new things he has thought of that he will ramble on for minutes. When he is finished, introduce him to the detective on the line at the local police department. That will be your last obscene call from him. All joking aside, telephone devices can be effective tools in aiding in the identification of such criminals. First, though, always check with the police before following such a recommendation.

By the way, I do work for a telephone company, but no, I am not on commission.

(The standard advice given by most phone companies regarding obscene calls is to hang up without saying anything. That is still a wise choice, but I wanted to make you aware of other intelligent options.)

PASSIVE WEAPONS

Other items that can be used as psychological weapons are police handcuffs, tie tacks, T-shirts and hats. Most of these have been, or will be, mentioned in other chapters. You are not to impersonate a police officer, but through the power of suggestion, you want a potential assailant to think you possibly could be an authority figure.

A good example of such methods of assault prevention would be to place a baseball-type police hat in the back window of your car when traveling out of state. Make sure it is turned at an angle that implies you really didn't want it to be to be noticed. If a potential assailant passes you on the highway, what is he going to assume?

If a potential assailant stops to assist you when you have had a car problem, what is he going think if he sees a pair of handcuffs on your turn signal or a "Chicago Police Department" T-shirt conveniently hanging on your clothes bar, facing toward the window? What would you do if you were a criminal?

There are many such inexpensive items that can greatly reduce your chances of becoming a crime victim. You are outsmarting your assailant, not outfighting him.

THE ULTIMATE WEAPON

The clerk in the convenience store had an uneasy feeling about the man at the magazine rack. He had been standing there for more than an hour. By now, it was 2:00 a.m. and fewer and fewer customers were coming in. As he walked away from the magazine rack, she thought he was finally going to leave. What a relief.

But instead, he walked up to the counter and calmly told her to come with him to the back of the store or he would kill her. He had his hand in his jacket pocket, but made no effort to expose a weapon. She felt that if she went with him, it would be all over for her. Company policy forbade the possession of a weapon, so she had nothing to defend herself with, except for one thing — her brain.

Sitting on the counter were a gallon jar of dill pickles and a gallon jar of jalapeno peppers. She grabbed the jar of pickles, raised it over her head and threw it at the surprised and panic-stricken assailant. He somehow avoided the jar, but was now several feet away after having retreated to avoid the blow. The gallon jar crashed to the floor, with broken glass and pickles flying.

The man started toward the counter, and instinctively she picked up the gallon jar of peppers, raised it over her head and told him to leave or she would kill him. Deciding she was going to be much more resistant to his demands than he had planned, he fled the store, to her relief.

This same assailant entered another convenience store at 2:00 a.m. three nights later. He forced the clerk to go around back to the restroom, where he raped and strangled her. As he left the restroom, a police officer on routine patrol pulled up and saw him. After finding the clerk in the restroom, the officer caught the assailant two blocks away as he hurriedly tried to escape. The convenience store clerk who had defended herself with the gallon jar of pickles identified the man as her attacker.

This true story may seem a bit anticlimactic for some, but the moral sums up the entire concept presented in this chapter and the others in

this book. By using your intelligence, your most effective weapon, and believing that you have a right to be left alone, you can do a great deal to avoid becoming a crime statistic.

YOUR INTELLIGENCE

Your brain as your ultimate weapon is far superior to any of the other weapons outlined in this chapter.

ADVANTAGES

1. Unlike a firearm, stun gun, or pepper spray, you always have your brain with you. The rare exceptions are those of us who have teenagers.
2. It is difficult to beat the price of using your own brain as the ultimate self-protection weapon, since it costs nothing.
3. You can practice using this weapon anytime, unlike the others. All you have to do is consciously be alert to dangers and think of ways to become more aware of crimes, avoid those dangers, and when necessary take the appropriate and prudent action.
4. Your size, age, sex or physical handicaps do not affect your ability to use the ultimate weapon, your brain.

By using your brain as the ultimate weapon, you can change daily habits that lend to your being victimized, thus making it harder for assailants to find victims. If you cannot eliminate the assailants, you must not provide them with prey.

Throughout this book, in each chapter, I always emphasize two main concepts:

You must strongly believe that you have the right to be left alone.

You must use your most precious weapon — your intelligence — to avoid becoming a victim of crime.

First, by studying the advantages and disadvantages of the weapons outlined in this chapter and making a studied and conscious decision in choosing one, you can have a great impact on your chances of becoming a victim of crime.

Second, if you are going to carry a weapon, know you will use it. Also, (3) make certain you have it when needed, (4) know the expected results, (5) know how to use it, (6) make sure you have practiced and are proficient with the weapon, and (7) have a backup plan in case the expected results fail to occur.

SUMMARY OF WEAPONS

First Choice:
YOUR INTELLIGENCE

Second Choice:
PEPPER SPRAY

Third Choice:
YOUR INTELLIGENCE

7

Tip 7

Determine Safe Locations Available 24 Hours a Day In Your City and On Frequently Traveled Routes

A teenage girl participating in one of my seminars recently told how a group of men followed her in another car one night. Upon realizing she was being followed, she sped up and drove at speeds in excess of 90 miles an hour. After driving more than thirty miles and finally deciding to take remote back highways, she eventually lost them. By then of course, she also was lost.

When she told me of the route she had taken, I asked her why she hadn't stopped somewhere for assistance. She replied that she hadn't realized there was anything she could do but try to outrun them. I then pointed out that in the first few miles of her escape route, she had passed one hospital, one large industrial plant and at least one fire station, all with 24-hour security personnel.

Her comment was the same as many others I have heard. "I had never thought about all those places having someone who could assist me." That is a typical response. We don't realize how much assistance is available until we take the time to plan for emergencies when traveling, whether driving in our automobiles, while walking or using commercial travel.

Because we spend much more time traveling than we did twenty years ago, it is necessary to develop assault prevention habits specifically for those times away from home. Your chances of being assaulted while away from home are greater than they have ever been.

Because of demographics and the development of suburbs, people now spend much more "windshield" time commuting to and from their jobs than they did ten or fifteen years ago. The more time spent commuting, the greater the opportunity for mechanical failure of your automobile. That presents a chance for a crime of opportunity for many assailants who specialize in preying on stranded motorists.

Because of the number of people who have to commute long distances to and from work, our highways and interstates have become so congested that violent crimes due solely to confrontations between motorists have become a daily occurrence in most major cities. Hardly a day goes by that someone isn't killed or seriously injured because of a disagreement over one driver swerving in front of another in rush hour traffic.

Many single parents trying to survive financially have to work late hours or two jobs, so more potential victims are available. Because some women, as well as some men, might not know the mechanics of keeping a vehicle in good working order, the chance for breakdowns can be greater, leading to more opportunity for an assailant posing as a good Samaritan.

Many people neglect their vehicle's working order. Once, gas station attendants would check under the hood and check tire pressure levels, finding dangerous problems, but that now is left to the driver, and many people feel they simply do not have the time to do those things.

Developing assault prevention habits while away from home could constitute a book in itself. While I can't cover all the aspects of that topic, I will attempt to cover some situations you could face and offer some possible courses of action.

WHEN FOLLOWED BY SOMEONE IN ANOTHER CAR

A common type of harassment and potential assault many people experience is being followed by someone in an automobile. Once, such activity was only a threat or harassment by teens out having fun at the expense of the "victim," whom they intended only to frighten. But today, in our crime-plagued cities, the seriousness of what was once considered a minor annoyance has become a real danger.

Now, being followed by a person or a gang in another car is not only frightening, but often culminates in such serious crimes as abductions, rapes and random "drive-by" shootings of innocent victims.

Having grown up as a driver in the '60s and '70s, I still find it hard to believe how violent people can become over something as trivial as honking a horn or swerving in front of another car. Today, even something as harmless as honking your horn while at a traffic signal can result in your being followed and even killed.

IF FOLLOWED WHILE DRIVING

Keep the following things in mind anytime you think or know you are being followed:

THE DON'TS

DON'T PANIC

This is not the time to lose your composure! You must now remember what was taught in this book. If you have read this chapter several times, the concepts are simple enough to remember, and they

will allow you to deal with someone following you.

DON'T TRY TO ESCAPE BY OUTRUNNING
THE PERSON FOLLOWING YOU

That not only endangers your life, but also jeopardizes other innocent motorists and pedestrians who might be accidentally injured or killed. You must outsmart and outthink your potential adversaries. Unless you are being shot at, you can rely on the safety of your automobile for the few moments you need to plan your course of action.

NEVER DRIVE TO
YOUR HOME IF FOLLOWED

Even if you are within blocks of your home before realizing you are being followed, continue to one of the "safe" locations I will discuss later in this chapter. Driving to your home, which is usually your first instinct, only allows the potential assailant to learn where you live. With just a little more time and information-gathering, the potential assailant can discover many more important facts about you.

It can be easy to determine if you live alone, your work schedule, where you work, if you have children, when you are away from home and other bits of useful information. If you avoid letting someone know where you live, while making sure the person gains no further knowledge about you, you will most likely have no further contact with him. These types of "animals" are looking for the easiest prey — one who will lead them to their den. With just a few "tricks" of your own, you can ruin the day for these kinds of criminals.

Once someone determines where you live or work, there is no law to keep them from following you there. And as long as they aren't breaking any laws, the police can do little. Even if someone intends you no harm, it is disturbing to be constantly followed. You can never be sure when or if their intentions will prove harmful. Being followed can become a form of mental assault, which is all the more reason to not let it happen.

DON'T IGNORE OR PRETEND TO NOT REALIZE YOU ARE BEING FOLLOWED

You must become proactive, not reactive.

DON'T STOP AND CONFRONT THE PERSON OR PERSONS

If someone is following or harassing you, never stop and try to determine his purpose. That is a good way to get yourself seriously injured or killed. Don't hit your brakes suddenly and try to intimidate him. That not only escalates the severity of the situation if he does stop before hitting your car, but it could also result in your automobile being struck from behind. Remember, from Tip 2, your car can be a barrier or trap for assault depending on how you use it. Don't make a serious mistake by acting immaturely or trying to prove you are not afraid of the person. Let your intelligence, not your temper, guide your actions.

THE DO'S

What action should you take to ensure that not only your, but also your family's, safety is protected in the event you are followed?

THE FIRST RULE IS TO KEEP YOUR COMPOSURE

It is best to outsmart, not outfight, your potential assailant. You will have already planned a course of action for just this kind of situation.

AS SOON AS YOU REALIZE YOU ARE BEING FOLLOWED, LET THE PERSON KNOW THAT YOU ARE AWARE OF HIS PRESENCE

Make eye contact if he pulls alongside you at a traffic light. Don't smile, just nod or stare with an air of confidence to let him know you are not intimidated. If he continues to follow, look in the rear-view mirror and slow down slightly to make him aware that you have noticed his presence. You should also make several unscheduled turns to let

him know that you know what he is doing. It is important when followed to immediately communicate that you have a plan and that it doesn't include him.

GET NEAR OTHER PEOPLE
AS QUICKLY AS POSSIBLE

It is always best to go to the nearest police station, fire station or any location that will have a police officer present.

Hospitals, industries with 24-hour security guards and schools, in the daytime, are also excellent choices if you don't know the location of the nearest police station. You will often have a much better chance of finding a fire station because of their required geographic disbursement throughout a city.

If none of those are available, your next best choice is a convenience store, grocery store, gas station or any location where other people are present. Remember from Tip 3, there is safety in numbers. Get near others as quickly as possible. The last thing an assailant wants is other people around to identify him or aid his intended victim.

BUY A CELLULAR
TELEPHONE FOR YOUR CAR

A good way to rid yourself of someone following or harassing you as you drive is to have a means of communicating with authorities immediately. Having a cellular telephone in your car can all but eliminate most forms of crimes against motorists. If you are being followed, being able to call for assistance while still in the safety of your automobile is well worth the investment.

Call a description of the person and car and your location in to someone, a friend or spouse, and advise them of your concern. That also serves as a deterrent, because now the person following you knows that he has been noticed and is not sure who you are talking to or what you are saying. That action usually is enough to rid you of being followed or harassed. And depending on the severity of the situation, call 911.

And in calling for assistance and giving your location for immediate help, think of the mental impact that has on the person following you.

If you have to, continue to drive around the block several times in the same area while waiting for assistance. It won't take long for the potential assailant to realize he is about to become the victim.

Cellular automobile telephones have spared thousands of stranded motorists the terror of assault by enabling them to call for immediate assistance following automotive trouble.

And if you can't afford a cellular telephone, there is still the citizen's band radio.   Although not nearly as effective in range and communications ability (sometimes the Samaritan who answers your call isn't the "good" one), the CB is still a means of communications in an emergency.

In many states, there is still a channel reserved for emergency transmission and monitored by volunteer groups. Just your action in communicating to "someone" leaves the possible assailant wondering who or what kind of assistance you have coming to your aid. You want to plant those seeds of fear, uncertainty and doubt in his mind.

If you can't afford a cellular telephone or CB radio, buy the cheapest telephone you can find and put it in your car.   Even an ordinary telephone receiver, with its cord attached, can serve to trick the assailant in an emergency.   The next time someone starts to harass you when you are driving, just reach under your seat, pull out the receiver and pretend that you are calling on your "cellular" telephone. Make sure the cord is hanging below the bottom of the window so no one but you knows it isn't hooked up to

anything. Many people put dummy antennas on their car to make the illusion even more effective.

Appearing to be talking on a cellular telephone while pointing to the possible assailant will serve the purpose. Make sure you point at the other car and its driver as you pretend to make your call. Especially at night, there is no way for the person to know for sure you aren't calling for assistance. That is usually enough to end the chase.

By now, the person or group following you is certain you have not only called for assistance but also have given 911 a description of them and their vehicle.

Being able to communicate immediately when traveling becomes even more important on vacation or out of your ordinary range of travel. Many assailants target victims with out-of-state automobile tags. Be extremely careful at night when traveling out of state and consult an automobile club about routes. Plan periodic stops at locations incorporated into your travel plans. Prepare not only to enjoy your vacation, but also make certain that an assailant doesn't ruin it for you.

ATTRACT A LOT OF ATTENTION

If you don't have a cellular telephone, until you can get to a safe location, attract as much attention as possible by flashing your headlights and honking your horn. Often that in itself will be enough to discourage the person following you. If you pass a police officer, get his attention. One woman who was being followed and had been shot at rammed a police car with her car. Needless to say, her pursuer disappeared. Although that is perhaps a bit extreme, if your life is in danger, do what you must.

If nothing else, stop in the middle of a busy intersection and block traffic. Someone is going to come to you for an explanation.

ON FREQUENTLY TRAVELED
ROUTES, KNOW SAFE LOCATIONS

Determine where the nearest locations for assistance are in case someone does follow you. Most people, like the young woman in the beginning of this chapter, have never thought about what to do if

followed. One woman in a seminar didn't realize that near her normal route to work were several industries with 24-hour security guards.

A man in one of my seminars described how he was followed for miles on an interstate by a car filled with teens. He feared for his life. When I asked if he had considered taking any exit along the route, he asked what help would that have been. When I mentioned the military base near by, he looked at me with total surprise.

Although he was fully aware of its location, he had never thought of it as a safe location. I assured him that all he had to do was continue through the sentry post without stopping and he would have attracted all the security he would ever want to see. Actually, all he would have had to do was stop at the gate and explain the situation.

You must prepare a plan of action. Having to think suddenly and under stress is difficult.

Occasionally take alternate routes home after work or shopping and determine the safe locations available in an emergency. If the need arises, you will already be aware of several locations that can provide immediate safety. It is a good practice to alternate your commonly traveled routes so that you don't set a pattern, and it also enables you to become more familiar with alternate routes for emergencies.

I commute sixty miles each way to work, and after taking alternate routes, I discovered at least a half-dozen plants with armed security guards, several fire stations and one police station that I didn't even know existed. All of those locations could provide immediate assistance in an emergency. Such assistance is useful in case of mechanical breakdown as well.

KEEP A PRACTICAL
WEAPON IN YOUR VEHICLE

One practical weapon to have in your vehicle is plenty of gasoline. The last thing you want to do is run out of gas while being followed. One of the most common crimes of opportunity is the assault of motorists who have had to walk for aid after running out of gas.

As many times as people have seen this tip mentioned in publications, it is still surprising how frequently people are assaulted,

robbed and slain because they ran out of gas on an isolated stretch of highway. Believe it or not, some criminals specialize in preying on stranded motorists.

Never let your gauge fall below one-fourth of a tank. Never see how far you can go on empty.

Other items to always keep in your car include the highway flare I mentioned in Tip 6. It can become an excellent weapon in an emergency if you are forced off the road. I keep a highway flare in each of my car door map pockets. I also have a pepper spray canister in the door pocket. Although I would hate to have to attempt to spray it through a partially lowered window, in an emergency situation it is an excellent weapon to have for protection while traveling by car or on foot.

And if someone forces his way into your car, spraying your pepper spray will certainly clear out all occupants.

Always try to keep a pen and notepad in your car for emergencies. That will enable you to write down information in case someone does attempt to follow you or run you off the road. Immediately write down pertinent information, such as the license number, color of vehicle, body style, description of the person and anything else you see. Those facts might be difficult to recall later.

If you do have to walk for assistance because you ran out of gas, you can leave a note for anyone who happens to stop to check on your disabled car. Just in case, you might leave a note that reads:

Ran out of gas. Will be right back.

B. Jones
Regional Parole Supervisor
Federal Bureau of Prisons

Would you take a chance?

And don't forget to leave your handcuffs on the turn signal and your police magazine on the front seat.

REPORT THE INCIDENT
TO AUTHORITIES

You should always notify local law enforcement agencies when you suspect you have been followed. That not only might help you in the event something does happen later, but the person might also be a threat to others and might have harassed or attacked people before. Often criminals roam from city to city committing the same crimes.

By reporting such incidents, you might be saving someone else the anguish of an assault or the terror of abduction of a child or family member. The only way to rid ourselves of crime is to work in unison with our law enforcement agencies. They cannot win the battle against crime without our help.

WHEN YOUR CAR BREAKS
DOWN AND BECOMES
THE "ASSAILANT"

I recently faced the problem of automotive failure for the first time in nine years of commuting sixty miles each way to work. I was traveling on the interstate at 65 miles an hour when suddenly my car went dead. I had never experienced this situation and at first I couldn't believe it was happening. Here I was at 4:30 p.m. on a Friday afternoon, in a torrential thunderstorm, halfway between two cities with no exits for five miles in either direction.

I managed to get to the right side of the interstate out of the traffic. After trying unsuccessfully to start my car, I realized that something was seriously wrong. And it wasn't a problem I could easily solve, such as a flat tire. Fortunately, I did have a cellular telephone in my car, but even then I didn't know who to call.

I sat for a few minutes, gathering my thoughts, and finally decided to call the dealership where I had the car serviced. They agreed to send a wrecker immediately, and within twenty minutes, assistance had

arrived. Waiting until you experience automotive trouble to plan a course of action is unwise, as I learned that day. I was prepared for any kind of assailant, but instead my problem was my own ignorance about what assistance I needed.

WHEN MECHANICAL FAILURE DICTATES THAT ASSISTANCE IS NECESSARY

The standard procedure or universally accepted practice is to raise the hood of your car, tie a white cloth to your antenna and turn your emergency flashers on. Then, if you don't have a way to summon help, you are at the mercy of a Samaritan who might stop and offer assistance. The only drawback I see to that method is that you are letting everyone know you are disabled, Samaritans and assailants alike. It is best not to stand outside your automobile and seek assistance.

Remember from Tip 2, your car can be a barrier or trap depending on how you use it. Remain in your vehicle even after someone stops, and ask them to call a wrecker. If someone offers to give you a ride, as tempting as it might be, never accept a ride from a stranger. Many people who did were never heard from again.

If you have never thought about who you would call for assistance, take the time to write down the telephone number of your car dealer or servicing center and put it in your glove box. That is especially important for teenage children, who usually have no idea what to do in such an emergency. They are quite frequently the victims of assailants simply because they have not had the experience adults have.

Take the time to discuss such problems with the other drivers in your family and make sure everyone knows what to do. If you are a member of an automobile club, make sure your teenage drivers are aware of the services they offer and how to reach the club. Automobile clubs are worth every penny when the need arises.

If you have a cellular car telephone and an automobile club membership, you have definitely reduced your chances of being victimized in the event your car breaks down. Although I didn't classify them as such, these are two of the best "weapons" you can have when

your car breaks down. Remember, a weapon is worthless if you don't know how to use it and don't have it available. Make sure you know who and how to call for assistance.

NEVER ACCEPT A RIDE WITH A STRANGER

A stranger could be a Ted Bundy or other serial killer.

An airline flight attendant, who fortunately had attended one of my seminars, told of her recent experience of running out of gas on a freeway in Dallas. It was early afternoon and she had just left the airport after being out of town for several days on a flight. She failed to check her gas gauge before leaving the airport and didn't notice it was on empty until she was on the freeway.

She was within a half-mile of the next exit when she ran out of gas. She could see a gas station sign at the next exit, so she decided to walk to the exit and seek assistance. As soon as she locked her car a man appearing to be in his seventies pulled up behind her, got out of his car and asked if he could be of assistance.

When the flight attendant told him of her dilemma, he volunteered to drive her to get some gas. The attendant, retelling the experience, said the one thing that kept flashing through her mind was from my seminar she had attended: "Never accept a ride with a stranger."

When she told the man thanks, but she would just walk to the exit since it was in sight, he became agitated and demanded that she accompany him. It was too "dangerous" for a woman to be walking on the freeway, he said. Something might happen to her, and besides, he had a can of gasoline at his house, which just happened to be nearby. They would drive there, get the gas and she could be on her way.

By now, he had grabbed her arm and was attempting to force her to accompany him. She broke loose, very firmly told him she wasn't going anywhere with him, and hurriedly began walking toward the service station. She said she was afraid to look back until she had

walked several feet from the man. When she looked back, he was cursing loudly as he returned to his car. He sped off shaking his finger at her, still cursing loudly.

She will never know what might have happened to her that day, but she felt that at the very least, she had been spared being the victim of an assault. Only that "concerned" old gentleman knows for sure what he had planned for her.

Assailants come in all sizes, shapes, ages and demeanors. Some of the most sadistic serial murderers are not only very intelligent, but quite often are nice-looking, professional-appearing people who have steady occupations when they aren't abducting and torturing unsuspecting victims. That is why it often takes years to apprehend a serial killer. They are not the everyday mugger who doesn't have enough sense to get in out of the rain. The sadistic assailant will often have an elaborate plan, but by following these basic assault prevention guidelines, you can avoid many such situations, like the one above.

OTHER TRAVEL TIPS

MOTORIST MUGGERS USE
SEVERAL COMMON TRICKS

I was describing in a seminar recently how assailants will use trickery to victimize unsuspecting motorists, when I noticed an elderly woman in the audience becoming pale. I was explaining how especially at night, an assailant will pull beside the intended victim's car while driving down the highway and point to a tire as though something is wrong with it. I explained that this is one of the most common ploys used to lure teenage girls into pulling over and checking their cars. Then the assailant pulls over to lend assistance, and by the time the victim realizes that nothing is wrong with the car, it is too late.

By now, the woman had raised her hand and impulsively screamed out, "That's what was happening." She detailed what had just happened to her and her sister as they returned from an out-of-state trip.

The two women were traveling together and were passing through a large metropolitan area around 1:00 a.m. on the interstate when a car with three men pulled alongside their car. The driver of the other car began honking and the man in the front passenger seat began pointing and motioning toward their rear tire, as though it was going flat.

They continued this behavior for several miles and finally sped away after the women did not pull over. Since the women could not feel the car riding any differently, they decided to wait until they reached an exit where a truck stop was located rather than pull over on the side of the interstate.

Of course, when they did finally stop at the truck stop, they were relieved to find out nothing was wrong with their car. Thinking nothing else of it, they continued on their journey and arrived safely at home. Not until a week later, while listening to my seminar, did the woman realize that what had occurred that night was a ploy commonly used by criminals to trick their intended victims.

Even though that woman was fortunate enough not to fall victim to the assailants, she was visibly shaken just thinking about what almost happened to her.

Never pull over to the side of the highway under such circumstances. Wait to examine your vehicle until you can reach an exit where there is a well-lighted gas station or truck stop. If you do have a flat tire, especially at night, drive slowly on the rim to the next safe stop.

ACCIDENTS IN
ISOLATED AREAS

Another favored method of criminals is to bump the intended victim's car from behind with their car. When you leave the safety of your car to check for damage, the assailant can complete the crime. Should you be involved in such a slight "bump" accident, drive to the nearest place with people. Especially at night, do not get out of your car. Remember **Tip 3, Always Use the Buddy System.**

POLICE OFFICER
IMPERSONATORS

A third method assailants often use to trick their victims is impersonation of a police officer. Anyone can buy a badge, dash-mounted flashing light and handcuffs at a police equipment supply store. Many rapists and child molesters pretend to be a police officer to abduct their victims. There are some general rules to always follow when stopped or questioned by someone who says he is a police officer.

If the person is in plainclothes and in an unmarked car, be suspicious immediately. Most detectives or vice officers who are in plainclothes don't make traffic stops. Unless you are a threat to cause serious bodily injury with your driving, a plainclothes officer is not going to pull you over for a traffic violation, such as running a stop sign. That is not their job. If you are driving that erratically, they will normally call for a patrol officer and monitor you until the uniformed officer arrives in a marked patrol car.

If you are stopped by an unmarked police car, rather than pull over immediately, drive to the next available public place. If a gas station or convenience store is in sight, continue to the parking lot instead of pulling over at an isolated location.

If a plainclothes officer requests that you get in his car for questioning, politely explain that you prefer to wait until a marked car with a uniformed officer is called. Then explain that you were once sexually assaulted by an assailant posing as a plainclothes police officer, and you were told by genuine officers to never get in an unmarked car. If this person really is a police officer, he won't have any problem with your concern.

If he isn't, now may be the time you have to deal with the threat of abduction or assault. Now it may become very important that you have read Tip 9 thoroughly.

Some assailants have elaborate schemes and can prove difficult to identify as police impostors. Remember serial killer George Kent Wallace? He would stalk teenage boys at grocery stores and use the

ruse of wanting to question them about their recent whereabouts because someone had provided their name as a possible suspect in a burglary in a nearby town. The killer would pose as a detective from another state and would tell them they were not under arrest, but needed to accompany him for questioning only. Once in the car, he would handcuff and legcuff his victims.

Never get in an unmarked police car with a plainclothes officer. Make sure your children are aware of that principle, and periodically reinforce it. We all teach our children to obey police officers, so impersonation of a police officer is a successful child lure.

THE DREADED RESTROOM STOP
WHILE AWAY FROM HOME

One last tip regarding safe locations when traveling is to be extremely careful when using public restrooms.

Public restrooms in shopping malls, highway rest stops, gas stations and public parks and campgrounds have become a haven for many criminals and crimes, such as prostitution, drug transactions, robbery and murder. Public restrooms are one place you **don't** want to **look like a victim**.

Sometimes when traveling on business alone or on vacation with your family, this is one dangerous area you just can't avoid. Nature seems to call at some of the most inopportune times, and doesn't it always seem that when you are on vacation, the kids "have to go" when it's 11:00 Friday night and you have no idea what interstate you are on, much less how far you are from the nearest town? Having to stop at a rest stop at 2:00 a.m. can be a nerve-racking experience.

As a former police officer, I know that many people like to travel at night because there is less traffic. I like to travel at night myself. I know that goes against DEFENSIVE LIVING, but often because of schedules, we have no choice but to travel at night. I used to see many military wives with small children traveling at night, stopping at rest stops to get a few hours of sleep. I would always patrol those areas with a greater degree of concern.

THINGS YOU CAN DO
TO MAKE YOUR VENTURE
A LITTLE SAFER

Do as much of your traveling in the daylight hours as possible. Remember **Tip 3, Always Use the Buddy System.** You want as many people around as possible. The cover of darkness brings out not only animal predators to hunt for prey, but human predators as well.

You should plan your stops before ever leaving on an extended trip, but emergencies do occur. If it is late at night, use restrooms at franchised restaurants. Many restaurants and chain motels are open twenty-four-hours a day. Many states now have interstate road signs that tell where such places are.

If you must stop at a roadside park, rest stop or other isolated location late at night, there are ways to not look like a victim. By now, after reading Tip 1 and Tip 6, you know what to have with you when you enter a dimly lit restroom.

In one hand you are going to have your pepper spray, and in a back pocket you are going to have a pair of handcuffs hanging in clear view of anyone who walks in. For a woman, you can hang the handcuffs on your purse.

Now, if you are a criminal thinking about victimizing someone that evening and waiting in a restroom, would you choose this person as a victim? If the assailant is outside in a car watching you go into the restroom, you want to make sure he sees the handcuffs as well. If you think that is a silly ploy, think about the alternatives and take my advice, it works.

If someone should ask if you are a police officer, by now you also know how to respond — "No, what do you think I am, a rocket scientist?" And if they then identify themselves as a police officer, explain why you carry the handcuffs. There is no law against carrying a pair of handcuffs as long as you aren't trying to arrest someone. They also make a good flailing weapon in an emergency and have many

practical uses when the children start to get on your nerves during the trip.

Travel safety tips would fill a book in themselves. But by using **Tip 7, Determine Safe Locations Available 24 Hours a Day In Your City and On Frequently Traveled Routes**, and the tips included in the other chapters, you can greatly reduce your chances of being victimized while traveling away from home.

8

Tip 8

Become Aware of Crime Trends and Criminal Characteristics

"If ignorant both of your enemy and yourself, you are certain in every battle to be in peril. When you are ignorant of the enemy but know yourself, your chances of winning or losing are equal. Therefore I say: Know the enemy and know yourself; in a hundred battles you will never be in peril."

Sun Tzu, *The Art of War*, 400 B.C.

In a certain metropolitan area, there had been a series of violent armed robberies at one particular chain of Mexican fast-food restaurants. All of the robberies were occurring on weekends and near closing time. On several occasions, customers had been pistol-whipped, then slain. Newspaper and television publicity regarding the incidents had been extensive.

A victim who survived one of the robberies witnessed the assailants robbing and pistol-whipping the employees, then systematically assaulting every customer in the restaurant, and finally beating and fatally shooting her husband.

The surviving victim had repeatedly warned her husband of the recent robberies at the restaurants and had suggested they eat somewhere else. His philosophy was reflected, just hours before he died, in his reply to her concern: "When it's your time to go, it's your time to go, and there is nothing you can do about it. Come on, let's go get an enchilada before they close."

Contrary to that unfortunate man and many others like him who espouse this fatalistic philosophy, there is much that can be done to lessen your chances of becoming a victim of violent crime.

Tip 8, Becoming Aware of Crime Trends and Criminal Characteristics can greatly reduce your chances of becoming a crime statistic.

When I present my seminar on "Choosing and Using a Weapon," I discuss the advantages and disadvantages of many different self-protection devices. I also introduce several items that can become a "weapon" in an emergency.

One such "weapon" is a newspaper. When I hold up an unrolled issue of a local newspaper, I ask the audience to think of at least four ways it can be used as a weapon in an emergency. While the newspaper is unrolled, the audience response is usually very limited at best. I then hold up a tightly rolled copy of that same paper and repeat the question. Occasionally, someone in the audience will then suggest that the rolled newspaper could perhaps be used as a bludgeon.

Believe it or not, by holding a tightly rolled newspaper in your hand and striking with one end as though you were pounding your fist on a door, you can use a newspaper to deliver very effective results to an assailant's face, chest, groin or temple.

By grasping both ends of the paper correctly and applying a choking technique to an assailant's neck, one can easily incapacitate and even kill if necessary.

In an emergency, you can also make a rolled-up newspaper a weapon by lighting one end for use as a torch to ward off a human or animal predator.

But the fourth and most effective way to use a newspaper as a weapon is to read it. Gaining knowledge of crime trends and criminal characteristics is one of the easiest forms of crime prevention to practice. By increasing your awareness of crimes occurring locally and regionally, you can take many precautions that will greatly reduce your chances of being victimized.

I demonstrate the newspaper as a weapon in my seminars to reinforce an important point emphasized throughout this book: You must use your intelligence.

By using your intelligence, you can learn to improvise and literally make anything a weapon in an emergency. But a more important concept is that you can learn ways to defeat an assailant without fighting.

As the quotation at the beginning of this chapter emphasizes, it is not only important to change your habits to reduce your chances of becoming a victim, it is just as important to study the habits of criminals and be aware of common crimes.

READ LOCAL CRIME REPORTS

KNOWLEDGE IS THE KEY TO PREVENTION

An easy way to gain insight into crime trends is to read the local newspaper's crime summaries. There is a wealth of information about property and personal crime in the police reports. These reports detail the crimes committed, and by studying the types and frequencies of such crimes and the methods used by criminals, you can heighten your awareness tremendously. Your awareness is important not only for you, but for your children.

My two boys are thirteen and fourteen, and to get them to read any section of a newspaper other than the sports section is next to impossible. Parents should educate their children and teach them etiquette and religion, but being aware of crime trends and criminal characteristics is also important.

Children should be made aware at an early age of what to do to reduce their chance of being victimized. Make them aware, too, of what constitutes a crime so they aren't, out of ignorance, accused of one.

For instance, when children approach the teen years, it is important that they know what constitutes sexual assault. It is devastating for a

young girl to be sexually assaulted, and it is equally devastating for her family. But it is also devastating for a young man and his family to experience the trauma of being wrongfully charged with sexual assault.

When you were a teen, did you really know when sex became a crime? How many of us as adults still don't know? Obviously quite a few, judging from the many sexual assault charges against prominent people. One such trial was broadcast live by a cable news network, and the trauma both families had to endure is impossible to measure. Both the victim and the accused will suffer for many years.

The last thing anyone wants to happen is for their young son to be accused of sexual assault because he didn't know it was a crime to have sex with a young girl unconscious from drinking too much alcohol. As quite often happens, getting caught up in peer pressure, young adults, both boys and girls, do things they would never consider doing otherwise. Make sure you discuss not only the characteristics of crimes, but also the consequences.

Peer pressure can make "criminals" out of "saints." In a highly publicized case of a gang rape of a young, slightly retarded girl, none of the five boys accused had ever been in any kind of trouble. These kinds of incidents are often the most difficult to understand. I'm sure several of the high school boys, who were also honor students, got caught up in the tremendous pressure to do what everyone else was doing. This surely doesn't justify the incident, but it does somewhat explain why such incidents occur.

Make sure you discuss such incidents with your young adults and make them aware of the pain and suffering all the "victims" will have to endure for the rest of their lives.

Make sure your children are aware of "guilt by association." I try to periodically review with my sons the fact that even though they may not be guilty of a crime, if they are with someone who committed one, they can be charged with that crime. The first time I told them this, my youngest son, who was ten at the time, just couldn't believe it.

If you can't get your children to read the newspapers or watch the news on television, it is your responsibility as a parent to make them

aware of crime trends and criminal characteristics. Make them aware not only of what sexual assault is, but also of the cons or ruses used by criminals to commit nonviolent crimes.

Talk with your children periodically about such subjects as satanic ritual crimes, and make sure they are aware that those crimes don't just occur in big cities. Watch for any signs of sudden change in dress, jewelry and the use of tatoos by your children or their friends. Peer pressure is one of the major causes of a good child going bad. Peer pressure isn't necessarily a criminal characteristic, but it can lead to trouble for your child in a very short time.

BE AWARE OF CRIME
TRENDS WHILE TRAVELING

Not only is it important to be knowledgeable of local crime trends, it is also important to be aware of national crime trends. One man recently realized that when he arrived in a major metropolitan area and on the way to his hotel was confronted by a mob protesting the arrest of a fellow gang member. The story had been on the front page of the

Would you assault the owner of this car?

local newspaper that morning, and it named the location where the protest was to take place.

If you plan to travel to a particular area on vacation or business, watch newspapers and television news reports for any information on major crimes occurring there. One of the first things to do when arriving at a destination, whether for an extended stay or just overnight, is to get a local newspaper and read the crime summary report and watch the local television news.

If you are an elderly man on vacation, the time to find out that there has been a rash of violent robberies of elderly male tourists in the city is before you become the next victim.

Likewise, if vacationing or traveling with your family, you don't want to discover after the fact that there have been multiple abductions of young children in the city you plan to visit.

When you are planning a trip or vacation to an area with a wonderful reputation for its amenities and leisure activities, be aware that criminals are also drawn to such locations. What better place to find victims than in a resort area?

If you know well in advance of a trip to a city that you have never visited, before making hotel reservations or sightseeing plans it is worth the price of a long-distance call to the local police department to determine if any particular area should be avoided. If you explain that you are new to the area, most police departments are extremely helpful, and who best can tell you where the problem areas are than the police?

If necessary, you can always exaggerate and tell them you are bringing a group of children to visit the city and are concerned for their safety. It is amazing to me, but most people are more worried about the weather when traveling than this much greater threat to their well-being.

Many corporations consider a city's crime rate more important than any economic or financial factor in deciding where to locate a new business venture.

CRIME STATISTICS

Some facts are good to know no matter where you are, simply because they are based on national statistics, not local crime reports. National crime statistics, released quarterly by the federal government, are a good barometer for determining generally which crimes are increasing and which are decreasing. Thousands of facts available from many different resources are published almost daily concerning crime in our country.

But you can't raise your awareness level if you don't read the information. Spend as much time reading these crime reports as you do reading the funnies in your paper and you can greatly increase your awareness of crime trends and criminal characteristics, thus reducing your chances of becoming a crime victim.

A FEW TO REMEMBER

AT LEAST HALF OF ALL SEXUAL ASSAULTS ARE COMMITTED BY SOMEONE THE VICTIM KNOWS

It is not always that stranger lurking in the dark who attempts or commits a sexual assault. Quite often, it is someone well known by the victim. Remember in **Tip 1, Don't Look Like a Victim.** If you tend to have a passive personality, learn to become more assertive. It can greatly reduce your chances of being sexually victimized by a "friend."

75 PERCENT TO 85 PERCENT OF SEX CRIMES AGAINST CHILDREN ARE COMMITTED BY SOMEONE THE CHILD KNOWS, LOVES OR TRUSTS

A man in one of my seminars confided to me that he was sexually assaulted as a child by a group of boys he had thought were his friends. He was ten years old at the time. He is now fifty, and after attending my seminar, he felt I was the first person he could talk to about the incident. He told of how that one incident had so greatly affected him that it altered not only his personality, but his perception of people. He said he has never trusted anyone since that day some forty years ago.

Nearly half of all sex crimes are committed by family members. Another thirty percent to forty percent are committed by acquaintances, baby-sitters, teachers, clergymen, doctors, etc. Make sure you periodically discuss those facts with your children.

I am always pleased that my seminars have helped someone avoid becoming a crime victim.   But I also leave many of the seminars carrying some of the sadness shared with me by many of the participants who have already become and still are "victims."

Please take the time to make your family members aware of crime trends and make sure you keep an open line of communication between yourself and your children should any of you ever become victimized. The recovery and healing process from criminal victimization is long and stressful for all involved.

And be certain to get counseling from a qualified source, no matter your age or however long it has been since the incident, or incidents.

THERE ARE AT LEAST FOUR KINDS OF PEOPLE WHO COMMIT RAPE, WHICH IS A CRIME OF VIOLENCE, NOT SEX

From the "ego" rapist, who is usually the least dangerous, to the "sadistic" rapist, who enjoys torturing his victims before killing them, there are as many different personalities of assailants as there are people in this world. No two assailants are alike, so don't plan on having only one method of defense.

Be prepared to deal with sexual assault as a crime of violence, not sex. You must use your ultimate weapon, your intelligence, and have already planned a course of action.

However, there is no way to predict what action should be taken in every situation. Study the enemy, study yourself and once you decide to take a course of action, do not hesitate.

BE AWARE OF, AND DISCUSS WITH YOUR FAMILY, METHODS AND "LURES" USED BY ASSAILANTS

Most abductions and sexual assaults are planned acts of violence.

They are not random, impulsive happenings in which you just "happen to be in the wrong place at the wrong time." Most serial rapists and murderers are intelligent people who plan their crimes in great detail. Only if you have planned a course of action, whether mental or physical, will you survive one of their deadly crime attempts.

Just as you try to study the cause and effect of certain diseases and adjust your diets and exercise programs to reduce your chances of being struck by a killer disease, you must also study the cause and effect of another form of killer, violent assault. Incorporate these DEFENSIVE LIVING habits into your "diet."

Some of the most common lures and methods used by assailants involve the FUD factors — fear, uncertainty and doubt, discussed in Tip 1. But also popular are lures that play on an adult's or child's senses of belonging and compassion. You must be aware of as many ruses as possible and never, never assume victimization can't happen to you.

LURES AND METHODS THAT RELY ON FEAR, UNCERTAINTY AND DOUBT

FEAR AND INTIMIDATION

One of the most common methods used by an assailant is the threat of violence or physical injury. Surprisingly, a large percentage of criminal assaults do not involve an actual weapon. Most are committed simply through verbal threat of physical injury if the assailant's demands are not met. When the intended victim is uneducated in alternatives or has never planned a course of action, the victim's only response will be based on his or her personality, not intelligence.

Children and adults faced with the threat of severe bodily harm are at a distinct disadvantage if they are unprepared to defend themselves intelligently. Magnify the severity of the situation with the presence of an armed assailant and the situation deteriorates further.

That is why it is so important to study Tip 1 and become proactive rather than reactive, with a planned course of action.

If you or your child are threatened with abduction by an armed assailant, you must have a planned course of action that will be not only effective, but safe. You or your child may have only a few seconds to make a decision that will affect both of you for the rest of your lives. Be prepared to face the threat of intimidation and fear tactics used by many assailants. Tip 9 goes into more detail in dealing with the threat of abduction.

IMPERSONATION OF AN AUTHORITY FIGURE

A second common lure used by assailants is portrayal of an authority figure. The impersonation of a police officer is one of the most common lures used by child abductors. We as a society have taught our children, just as we were taught, to respect and obey authority figures. A police officer is to be trusted and obeyed.

The constant game of chess being played by some criminals and their police counterparts presents an interesting paradox. The criminal on one hand often uses the guise of portraying a police officer to complete his crime against an unsuspecting victim, and at the same time, the undercover police officer is often using the same methods of trickery to catch the unsuspecting criminal by pretending to be the perfect victim.

This shows how even the experts, whether it is the criminal trying to commit the crime or the police trying to prevent the crime, often rely on role-play to achieve their objectives. You, too, must develop role-play to avoid becoming a crime statistic.

Make sure you discuss with your children, and remember yourself, the fact that you should never accompany a "police officer" out of uniform anywhere from the public eye. Show due respect, but firmly demand that a uniformed officer in a marked car be present. If the officer demands that you enter his unmarked car for questioning, politely request a marked patrol car and remain outside the vehicle.

Once you explain your actions, a legitimate law enforcement officer will have no problem with your concern for your own safety. If he is an impostor, he will probably abandon the plan. It is too easy to find another victim who will obey his demands.

If the "officer" appears to hastily drop his investigation, make sure both you and your children know to gather as much information as possible, such as license number, type of car and a description of the person. Your ability to react intelligently and gather information could save someone else the horror of becoming his next victim.

You have to be aware that criminals often not only portray authority figures, but quite often actually are authority figures. Child molesters come in all ages and professions. Read your local and national newspapers and every week you will see where some clergyman, teacher, baby-sitter, relative, next-door neighbor, day-care worker or even parent is accused and proven to be a child molester.

Be alert to signs of an abnormal interest in your child by anyone and of an adult or older child spending time isolated with your child. Frequently discuss with your children the concept of improper touching and why it is not okay.

THE EMERGENCY LURE

Using a ploy designed to plant fear, uncertainty, and doubt in the mind of the intended victim, many assailants will pretend to be a utility

repairman needing access to the home to check for "dangerous" conditions, such as a gas leak or contaminated water. Also, the "emergency" ploy is used to trick an unsuspecting motorist into pulling over to check for a mechanical or tire failure, only to be assaulted by the "Samaritan."

Some of these ploys were discussed in Tip 7. Countless victims have been assaulted, raped, and murdered through the lure of a minor "fender-bender" after an assailant has purposely bumped the victim's vehicle. Especially at night, never get out of your vehicle after a minor accident. Drive to a place of safety, such as a convenience store or gas station where there are other people.

It doesn't matter if local laws prohibit leaving the scene of an accident. I would rather my child be ticketed for moving a car involved in an accident than to have him assaulted or abducted. Once you have an opportunity to explain, most officers are understanding.

Be aware that this is a very common criminal method used to commit sexual assaults, robberies and abductions. As I continue to stress throughout this book, mental, not physical, superiority is the key to assault prevention.

The feigning of an "emergency" involving a parent to trick or lure a child is also a common method used by criminals. Make sure your family has an established "password" that strangers must use before you or a family member accompany them.

One young girl avoided becoming a statistic by having a planned course of action in case of an emergency. While walking home from school, she was confronted by a man who pulled up in a car and said her mother had sent him to pick her up.

Because of planning, she immediately asked the man if her mother's name was Betty. He confirmed that indeed her mother's name was Betty and urged her to get in the car since he was late in picking her up. The mother's name was Marsha, and the girl quickly reversed her direction and began calling for help. The assailant escaped and two days later abducted a young girl walking in the same vicinity. She was sexually assaulted, but released alive.

As a former elementary school principal, I know the anger and

frustration experienced when an abduction occurs, especially when a parent or relative feels responsible for the incident.

A father came to pick up a fourth-grader one Friday afternoon immediately after lunch. He said there had been a death in the family and they had to travel out of state for the funeral. I had met the mother several times but had never met the father, and had no idea the couple was divorced. He was from out of state, and custody of the child had been granted to the mother. The incident happened so routinely that in a few minutes the child, showing no fear or emotion, quietly left with her father.

Only at the end of the school day, when the mother arrived to pick up her daughter, did I discover what a terrible mistake I had made. Fortunately for me and the child, the father was apprehended that evening before he could get across the state line. I can assure you that never happened to me again. I was fortunate that the incident had a happy ending, because I would probably still be looking for the girl had her father not been caught.

The next week, I established a "password" system and other security measures to ensure that children were released only to authorized adults.

Countless children have been kidnapped using the same or similar methods. It is important that those responsible for children's safety — whether at school, day care, church functions or just a bunking party — be conscious of how harmless a threatening situation might appear and how easily you could inadvertently release a child to someone other than a legal guardian.

LURES CRIMINALS USE
BASED ON COMPASSION
AND BELONGING

ATTENTION/AFFECTION LURE

A common non-threatening lure that assailants use is showing special attention to a victim. Both children and adults are equally vulnerable to this age-old technique. Children from broken homes and adults with unhappy marriages are often the target of molesters. It is

now understood that the majority of child molesters and sex offenders, once referred to as "dirty old men," were themselves the victims of sexual abuse as children.

Because the victim is quite often starved for affection or attention, he or she becomes easy prey for the molester. Anyone can be a molester, and that in itself makes it difficult to recognize until after the crime has occurred.

Make sure you discuss with your children the importance of telling you about any form of improper touching or suggestive verbal conversation by anyone. It is critical that you have this line of communication with your children established. The molester often uses subtle methods in the early stages of determining the vulnerability of a victim.

Remember the importance of the concept of "morality" in **Tip 1** and make sure you and your children believe strongly that you and they have the right to be left alone. Your children must communicate to a potential assailant that they **Don't Think and Look Like a Victim.**

Be alert to excessive hugging, requests for physical affection and excessive compliments about the physical appearances of both you and your child. If your child confides to you that he or she has been sexually abused or molested, take is seriously. Concocted stories of molestation are not the norm. Most experts agree that children rarely lie about such incidents.

ASSISTANCE LURES

Playing on an intended victim's compassion is also a common ploy by assailants. Sex offenders have done everything from asking a child to help look for a lost pet to hiring the intended victim as a baby-sitter.

One young girl recently disappeared in a small town in Arkansas as she went door to door selling raffle tickets for a school function. Her body was found a few days later in a ditch near the city limits. I would be willing to bet that one of the lures discussed in this chapter was the method the killer used to abduct the child. Make sure you frequently discuss with your children the dangers presented by pleas of assistance from criminals whose sole purpose is to harm them.

BRIBERY LURE

At the opposite end of the spectrum from the intimidation lure is the bribery lure, which is also an effective method employed by the sex offender. If you can't frighten them into submission, buy their trust. Money is quite often the root of this evil. Offers of toys, pets, money and candy are still tools of the trade for many sex offenders. Make your children aware that very few things in life are free, and the price they pay for an ice cream cone could be their life.

I recently role-played as an assailant for a friend to confirm that his five-year-old would not get in the car with a stranger. I tried to coax the young boy to accompany me for a ride in my new car. He refused to come near my car, as he had been taught, but also failed to immediately enter his house. That gave me one last opportunity to lure him.

I promised him an ice cream cone and assured him I would bring him right back. That was all it took. Thank goodness that was only a role-play. Do you know what your child would do under the same circumstances? If not, find out in a similar manner.

In my assault prevention seminars for children, that is exactly what I do. I teach children several ways to recognize and escape an abduction attempt when the lures outlined in this chapter are used. In a very short time, the children are aware of the ploys and are able to defend themselves against many of these lures.

For teenagers and adults alike, appealing to the ego and one's sense of belonging to a group is an effective method of bribery. Sex offenders often promise rewards of fame and fortune to unsuspecting victims enticed to model for photographs. Not only teenagers, but adults fall prey to this scheme.

Let common sense prevail when you are approached with promises of fame and stardom. How realistic could it be for a complete stranger to approach you and make you an overnight superstar in the modeling or entertainment business? Ask some of the superstars who washed dishes in Hollywood restaurants for years before being discovered and they will quickly tell you. It just doesn't happen.

As I point out in several tips, our personalities often get us into trouble. We all at one time, in moments of weakness, like to think that we could become a star in our own right if only given a chance.

These are far from all the lures used by sex offenders, but hopefully enough have been described to make you realize how important being aware of them is in preventing you or a family member from being victimized. Please take the time to occasionally review the methods in this chapter, and be alert to other lures you see or read about in the news. Sadly, I'm sure that soon after reading this book, you will be reading or seeing the details of some crime committed with the use of a lure.

BE AWARE OF
SEASONAL CRIMES

A dangerous time of the year to be victimized is near Christmas. More robberies and purse snatchings occur around Christmas than any other time of the year. Take extra precautions to reduce your chances of looking like a victim.   Often the assailant wants only your possessions and has no intentions of harming you unless you provoke him. Always have a small amount of "mugger money" or costume jewelry readily available to appease an assailant.

Often, people turn to crime after becoming depressed and desperate. And in times of economic despair and massive layoffs, more people feel forced to commit crimes to meet their obligations.

Knowing when particular crimes are most prevalent can help you. Be aware that sexual assaults tend to increase considerably in the summer. Most occur on weekends, late at night.

SOURCES OF INFORMATION
FOR CRIME TRENDS AND
CRIMINAL CHARACTERISTICS

The importance of learning as much as possible about crime trends and assailants should be clear to you by now. There is no way to include in this book all the information that is available, but there are

many good sources of information. I have listed below some sources and have included sources that can be of benefit whether you are interested in ways to avoid becoming a victim or have been victimized and need legal or emotional counseling.

LOCAL NEWS

A sound source for crime information and trends is your local news. Be aware of crimes happening in your city and area and take the necessary precautions to avoid becoming the next victim.   Local newspaper reports and television specials on crime prevention continue to be some of the best and most readily available sources of information to increase awareness of crime.

POLICE AGENCIES

The police department is also one of the best available sources for information on crime and crime prevention. Most departments have excellent, and free, crime prevention programs and material. Police agencies cannot be held completely responsible for taking the total "bite" out of crime. It takes citizens working with the various police agencies as a team to help them help us. The police can't be everywhere at the same time.

If there is one professional who is underpaid and unrecognized for the job he does, it has to be the police officer. You could double every police officer's salary and it still wouldn't even come close to paying them appropriately for the job they perform. Until you have walked in their shoes, you can't begin to appreciate the debt we all owe these men and women.

UNITED STATES GOVERNMENT AGENCIES

The Justice Department publishes extensive crime reports based on information from crime information centers in all 50 states. An annual sourcebook of criminal justice statistics is available to everyone, along with periodic Bureau of Justice statistics, by writing to the Justice Statistics Clearinghouse, National Criminal Justice Reference Service, Box 6000, Rockville, MD 20850.

THE NATIONAL VICTIM'S RESOURCE CENTER

The center is a national clearinghouse for victim's information financed by the Office for Victims of Crime, U.S. Justice Department. Like the Justice Statistics Clearinghouse, the NVRC is one of several information resources maintained by the National Criminal Justice Reference Service. When you call or write the NVRC, information specialists will provide you with access to the following resources:

- More than 7,000 victim-related books and articles covering child physical and sexual abuse, victim's services, domestic violence, victim-witness programs and violent crime included in the NCJRS data base.
- National victimization information.
- Federally sponsored victim-related research studies.
- Names, addresses and telephone numbers of people to contact for information and assistance.
- Information on state victim's compensation programs financed by the Office for Victims of Crime.

You can also get free publications, borrow hard-to-find publications and buy selected videotapes.

For more information call (800) 627-NVRC (6872) or write to National Victim's Resource Center, Box 6000-AJE, Rockville, MD 20850.

NATIONAL ORGANIZATION FOR VICTIM ASSISTANCE

NOVA is a non-profit, public-interest, membership organization that is based on volunteer efforts and individual contributions. Founded in 1975, its membership includes victims of crime, representatives of the criminal justice system, health and mental health professionals and victim advocates, as well as the lay public.

NOVA is dedicated to four purposes:

- National Advocacy — serving as the voice for victims in

state legislatures and the U.S. Congress.
- Direct Services for Victims of Crime — providing twenty-four-hour crisis counseling and follow-up assistance to victims of all types from all states, when local programs are unavailable.
- Professional Development — helping to establish new programs and expand existing services to better meet the needs of crime victims.
- Membership Communication - providing up-to-date information on new ideas, programs and knowledge in the field of victim assistance.

Each year NOVA helps over 10,000 victims of crime through its direct services. In the past, NOVA staff and members were major leaders in passing the federal Victim and Witness Protection Act of 1982, the Victims of Crime Act of 1984 and Bills of Rights for victims in almost every state.

Despite the fact that NOVA's resources are limited, its volunteers and members continue to be extraordinarily effective in providing assistance to crime victims.

For more information, or to join, contact Cindy Arbelbide, Director of Training, 1757 Park Road N.W., Washington, D.C. 20010, (202) 232-6682 ("232-NOVA").

JUST DYING FOR AN ENCHILADA?

Don't be your own worst enemy and ignore all of the valuable information available to you on crime trends and criminal characteristics. Even worse than being uninformed is being informed and not using the information, just like the man in the example at the first of this chapter.

As Sun Tzu might say if he were alive today:

*"Before we can defeat the enemy,
we must first know who he is."*

9

Tip 9

When Confronted with Abduction, Never Leave a Public Area, Even when Threatened with Death or Injury

It was a Wednesday afternoon around 1:30.

He had driven around all morning and had no luck so far. He was not even sure what town or state he was in. It really didn't matter. He had become angry because he wanted to find a victim before the day was over.

It had been about a week since he had escaped from the State Institution for the Criminally Insane, and he had already victimized three women.

Three days had passed since he had attacked his last victim. "They will never find her body," he thought. He often talked to himself. "They were such willing victims, doing exactly as I told them to. What ignorant women. I hate them all. My mother hated and abused me, so they are only getting what they finally deserve."

As he passed a small shopping mall, he decided to park his truck in

front of one of the stores and wait for a victim. Immediately, a young woman pulled in and parked her car next to his truck. "Perfect," he thought, "all by herself." He already knew how he was going to abduct her. It had worked every time.

There were ten to fifteen people within twenty feet, walking to and from their cars. As she got out of her car, he got out of his truck. As she walked to the front of her car toward the mall, he moved between his truck and her car. Politely, pointing to the rear tire of her car, he inquired, "Miss, do you realize you have a flat tire back here?"

As she walked back to examine the tire, he grabbed her and placed a large hunting knife to her ribs. The words still echo in the victim's mind years later. "Get in the truck, down in the floorboard, or I'll kill you."

The victim of that abduction and sexual assault still carries the physical and mental scars, ten years later. If she ever recovers mentally, it will be a miracle. Had she used the method outlined in this chapter, the abduction would have been prevented and her life and her family's life would be different today.

DEFENSIVE LIVING was written primarily to help people avoid situations just like this one. Countless crimes are committed against people every day, and no one book can address all situations and offer solutions to those crimes. But, by using simple methods of avoidance and having a plan of action, you can all but eliminate the crimes associated with abductions.

If you will study this chapter, it alone will be worth the price of the book. Then if you, your child or a friend are ever confronted with the threat of abduction, you will be forever grateful for the small investment you made in this book.

The methods presented in this chapter have saved many people from serious injury and death. Many of these people had previously thought they had no alternative but to do as told by an abductor. Many others, who unfortunately did not know of these alternatives, obeyed the assailant and did not live to tell about it.

Please read and discuss the concepts presented in this chapter with your family, especially your children, who are so vulnerable to the crime of abduction. As I am writing this book, I continue to see evidence of the trend of abductions daily in the newspapers and on television.

"A ten-year-old girl walking to school abducted. Found two days later at a garbage dump, raped and killed."

"A young mother abducted as she walks to her car at a shopping mall. Found the next day, raped and killed."

"A forty-year-old executive of a Fortune 500 company abducted as he walked to his car in a parking deck. The demanded ransom paid but his body found three days later."

And countless unknown victims who are still unaccounted for, with no one knowing if they ran away or were abducted. The list goes on and on, and it may happen to you!

You must begin to store this tip in your mind. Then you and your loved ones will not be abducted. Neither you nor your child will ever get in the car with an abductor.

THE CRIME OF ABDUCTION

Many times, a criminal cannot complete the intended crime for fear of being discovered. By abducting the victim, the assailant can then isolate the person, thus providing the opportunity for robbery, assault and murder.

By becoming aware of common methods used in abductions, you can avoid many of the situations.

No one solution is 100 percent guaranteed. However, a study of ways to avoid abduction can lead to effective courses of action and a way of thinking that can prevent such crimes.

ABDUCTION METHODS

As an intended victim approaches his or her vehicle, or is getting out of the vehicle, an abductor will approach and threaten both verbally and by exposing a weapon. It usually occurs suddenly, and the victim has **one to five seconds** to make one of the most important decisions in his or her life. There is no time to think about options, and most frequently victims obey because they don't know there is an alternative. With the verbal threat of death and the presence of a weapon, it is easy to see why most people would comply.

At the beginning of my seminars, I ask how many people would get in the car if told, and almost 100 percent say they would. By the end of the seminar, 100 percent are confident in their ability to avoid being abducted and know there is no way they would go with an abductor.

In a second common method, the abductor will enter through an unlocked driver or passenger door of the victim's vehicle as it is either parked or at an intersection.

The advantage of having your doors locked will give you the few seconds necessary to realize something is happening to you and will provide you time to escape. It is hard to believe, but many people who are abducted did not have their car or home doors locked. Remember from Tip 2, your car or home can be a barrier or trap, depending on how you use it. Once someone is in your car with you, it definitely has become a trap.

A third method is the abductor's using his vehicle to commit the abduction. This is one of the easiest to avoid once you have a plan. The criminal usually has a plan. You must have a superior one.

Abductors often prefer this method of abduction because they feel much more in control. They are in their car, or quite often a stolen car, and thus are more concealed than if they simply walked up to a victim's car. They obviously have a much quicker way to escape in case the abduction doesn't go as planned.

And the car gives them the cover to have, and threaten to use, a weapon without the public seeing. This method, used with a lure, is the most common one used to abduct women and children. Drive-by abductions are responsible for thousands of deaths, sexual assaults and

beatings.

The assailant wants and needs to isolate you to complete his crime. The assailant who threatens you with death or injury unless you do as told is counting on your ignorance of alternatives. No matter what method of abduction you are faced with, remember one important fact:

GOING WITH THE ASSAILANT IS NOT AN OPTION

After being told to never accompany an abductor, most people react with disbelief. Their first comment is always the same: "If you don't go with the assailant and he has a gun, he is likely to shoot you."

My answer is also always the same. Common sense tells me that if an abductor would take the chance of shooting you on a mall parking lot or at a child playing in a front yard, then what would he do if he gets you to a deserted area? If the assailant is crazy enough to shoot a victim in clear view of others, then be assured that your chances of surviving by complying with his demands are limited.

You are much less likely to be injured or sexually assaulted by staying in the public eye than by accompanying the abductor. Even the sadistic assailants, who are the most dangerous and unpredictable, prefer to isolate their victims, so they can torture them before fatally injuring them.

Even a Ted Bundy-type assailant will abandon an abduction plan if he perceives that there might be witnesses. The assailant needs to remove the victim from other people, who might either identify him, or worse, come to the victim's aid.

WHAT ARE THE ALTERNATIVES?

VERBAL REFUSAL

An easy method would be to simply refuse to go and see what happens next. When told to get in the car, look the assailant in the eye and firmly say, "No, I am not going anywhere." By using this method,

you have immediately communicated that things aren't going as he had probably hoped.

Now, depending on the personality of the assailant, he has three options. He can attempt to physically force you to accompany him. He can forget it and escape and make another attempt with a different victim who will obey his commands. Or he may decide to abandon the attempted abduction, but still harm you for not complying — probably not as severely as if you accompanied him, but you have still created an instant adversarial role between you and the assailant.

Depending on your personality, this might be your natural instinctive reaction. A person with a "Type A" personality would tend to choose this alternative even with little or no training.

The inherent danger in choosing such an option is the creation of a situation in which the assailant must now make a decision to fight or run. Depending on his personality, the chance for confrontation — and thus physical contact between you and the assailant — is a real possibility.

Because of the last possibility, I recommend the alternative of verbal refusal only as a last resort. Remember from Tip 5, the longer that contact with the assailant is prolonged, the less your chances of escaping injury or death.

PHYSICAL COUNTERACTION

You could choose to use physical counteraction or a self-protection weapon, finally getting to put into practice all the "deadly" techniques you learned in your self-defense courses.

If the assailant is unarmed, then that option is a real possibility. But remember, you still stand a good chance of being injured even if you win the battle.

Karate, pressure point tactics, and other self-defense techniques are much more difficult to recall and carry out in a life-or-death confrontation. In such a situation, you are forced to rely on a technique you may have been briefly introduced to years ago.

DISADVANTAGES OF CHOOSING PHYSICAL COUNTERACTION

A sexual assault occurred on a college campus in clear view of several dozen witnesses. When asked why they did not intervene, all said they thought that both parties were consenting partners because they were out on the lawn in front of a fraternity house and the woman was not requesting assistance.

Often, people witnessing a physical confrontation will avoid the quarrel, not knowing if it is a personal argument or an actual assault by a stranger. People also hesitate to intervene in a physical altercation for fear of being injured themselves.

A Major League Baseball umpire was severely injured while attempting to aid a robbery victim. Upon seeing a woman being assaulted, he and a friend immediately went to her aid and pursued the assailant, only to be shot several times by the assailant's accomplices. I'm sure that if the occasion ever presents itself again, he will think twice before deciding to be a good Samaritan. Few people today are willing to risk their lives to assist a stranger.

You might whip out your trusty handgun, but how often do you have it available? Remember **Tip 6? If You Are Going to Carry a Weapon, Know How to Use It and Have It Available.**

If you possess a self-protection weapon and are not sure you will use it, then it is of no value to anyone, except possibly the assailant. You must be sure the weapon is not taken away and used against you.

Another thing to consider before choosing to use physical counteraction is the liability you might face if you fight and inadvertently use too much force or, worse, harm an innocent bystander. A man was recently mugged and as his assailant was escaping, the victim pulled a gun and shot at the fleeing mugger. The shot missed the intended victim, but struck an eleven-year-old girl standing across the street. She was killed instantly.

I relate these instances not to dissuade you from exercising the right of self-defense, but to make you aware that there are advantages and disadvantages to every kind of self-protection.

PASSIVE RESISTANCE

It was a Wednesday afternoon around 1:30. It had been about a week since he had escaped from the State Institution for the Criminally Insane, and he had already victimized three women.

As he passed a small shopping mall, he decided to park his truck in front of one of the stores and wait for a victim. Immediately, a young woman pulled in and parked her car next to his truck.

There were ten to fifteen people within twenty feet, walking to and from their cars. As she got out of her car, he got out of his truck. Politely, pointing to the rear tire of her car he inquired, "Miss, do you realize you have a flat tire back here?"

As she walked back to examine the tire, he grabbed her and placed a large hunting knife to her ribs. "Get in the truck, down in the floorboard, or I'll kill you."

The woman pleaded, "I'll do whatever you say. Please, don't hurt me." As she turned to look at him, her eyes rolled up and she fainted, crumpling to the ground. The other people near the scene immediately noticed her lying on the ground with a man standing over her. Some began to stare. Others started her way to see if there was anything they could do or to offer medical help. Suddenly, the assailant ran to his truck, jumped in and sped away — alone.

My third and preferred option is the use of passive resistance. When I speak of passive resistance, I mean a method that defeats the assailant's plan without directly challenging the assailant, either verbally or physically — a method that has been proven effective time after time in both seminars and actual incidents.

One of the easiest and most effective ways for a man, woman or child to avoid being abducted is to simply pretend to faint when confronted.

What if the woman in the story had faked a faint, rather than going with the assailant?

Before you scoff at this solution, take a moment and put yourself in the place of an assailant attempting an abduction. If your intended victim has just fainted and is lying on the ground, and people are staring and approaching, what would you do? How long are you going to hang around?

I have simulated this situation thousands of times in my seminars with unsuspecting volunteers who agree to portray the abductor, and the results are always the same: Total shock and disbelief. They were expecting me to either do as I was told or fight back.

Their first comment, when asked what they would do next as the abductor, is also always the same: "I would get the heck out of there as fast as possible." The result is complete surprise and frustration for the assailant.

WHY FAINTING IS SO EFFECTIVE

YOU ARE GOING TO BE
DIFFICULT TO ABDUCT

By falling to the ground and becoming limp, you have greatly reduced your availability. The assailant now has to decide to either somehow pick you up and get you in the car or abandon the plan and escape. In almost all cases, the assailant is going to abandon the plan. Now he is the one faced with the one to five seconds to make an important decision.

Have you have ever tried to pick up a ten-year-old child who has fallen asleep on the floor watching television? If so, you can understand how difficult it is to pick up someone who is totally relaxed. Lifting a limp adult is practically impossible.

By fainting, you have removed yourself from the immediate danger of being physically forced into a car or a building. The assailant's greatest foe is time. How quickly can he isolate you to avoid being discovered? The longer it takes to complete the abduction, the better your chances of surviving the attack.

YOU AVOID A CONFRONTATION
WITH THE ASSAILANT

You greatly reduce your chances of injury. By fainting, you have not challenged the assailant or forced him into violence. Just the opposite: By fainting you have made him believe that he has already injured you. If you have properly role-played, as I will outline later in this chapter, the assailant will believe he has perhaps even killed you. That is exactly what you want him to think.

If the assailant is armed, fainting gives you the opportunity to remove yourself from direct contact with the weapon. If he is armed with a gun or knife, fainting removes you from harm immediately. Many injuries occur during abductions simply from being in the line of fire from nervous, deranged or drug-crazed assailants.

YOUR CHANCES OF GETTING
HELP ARE GREATLY INCREASED

Think about it for a moment.   Most people witnessing a confrontation between two people will avoid the quarrel, as I discussed in Tip 1.   By pretending to faint, you trick the assailant and others around you.

What do most people do when they see someone lose consciousness? They rush to the person's aid to see if they can help. Everyone suddenly becomes a doctor. In fact, studies have shown that more than half of the people who claim to be a doctor at the scene of an accident or a medical emergency have had little or no medical training.

The last thing an assailant wants to look up and see is people rushing to try to help. You can imagine the first thing on the assailant's mind: Escape as quickly and quietly as possible.

FAINTING IS EASY TO PERFORM

Fainting is much easier to practice than trying to kick someone in the groin, and possibly missing, or trying the "deadly" pressure point technique you learned years ago that probably doesn't even work. It takes little physical dexterity or time to become proficient at a pretend faint. It isn't something you have to practice daily.

Of course, you may actually lose consciousness without any practice at all if an assailant approaches you. It will probably be the smartest thing you have ever done.   And when accompanied by verbal reinforcement, as discussed later in this chapter, it is even more effective.

FAINTING IS AN EFFECTIVE DETERRENT
FOR MEN, WOMEN OR CHILDREN

I have conducted many experiments and have found the method almost as foolproof as any. Your size, sex or age does not decrease its effectiveness. The objective is to not leave the public view. Once you are out of sight, you are at the assailant's mercy.

The technique is especially effective for children. For instance, many abductions of children occur at shopping malls, schools and theaters. If you were to see a child being escorted out of a mall, fighting and resisting, you might easily think the adult is a parent finally fed up with a spoiled brat just wanting his way. Many children have been abducted just this way, never to be seen again.

Had that child known what to do, the abduction would never have happened.   By feigning a faint, or perhaps a seizure, the child accomplishes several lifesaving objectives. It distances them from the potential abductor. It creates a situation that makes an abduction almost impossible. And it attracts a different kind of attention. Now, people naturally approach to render aid rather than thinking just another child is having a tantrum. You are outsmarting both the assailant and others around you by enlisting their aid.

If the would be abductor happens to be a sadistic assailant, which quite often is the case just because of the nature of the crime, then it is of the utmost importance that you do not leave the public eye. Many abductions are successful simply because the victim has never thought about the possibility, and has no plan.

HOW TO USE FAINTING TO AVOID ABDUCTION

AVOIDING THREE COMMON METHODS OF ABDUCTION

ENTERING YOUR CAR

The first situation I raised was one in which you are entering your car and someone confronts you and demands that you get in the car or they will harm you. Remember, they are counting on you doing exactly as told, and time is critical for both the potential assailant and you. The first **one to five seconds** of this confrontation will now determine whether you survive or not. You must already have a plan and be prepared to execute it.

The first thing you do is to verbally reassure the assailant that you are going to comply. Your comment when faced with a forced abduction should always be the same: "I will do anything you say, just don't hurt me, please."

This serves two important functions. It immediately lowers the chances the assailant will physically harm you and it sets up your plan to outsmart the assailant.

The first five seconds of the confrontation are extremely important to the assailant, because he is quite often nervous. Your first goal is to calm him and prevent him from harming you. If you were to immediately begin physical counteraction, you might avoid being abducted, but you might also get yourself killed.

By saying you are going to comply, you reinforce his belief that you are going to be a willing victim, decreasing your chances of being harmed when you "accidentally" fail to go along with his demands.

You also bring mental warfare into play. You inform the assailant that you are not well, which again reinforces his belief that you will be an easy prey. You are setting up your plan, as well as planting in the mind of the assailant the idea that you cannot threaten him.

The last thing you tell the assailant is that you are recovering from a serious illness. Your last statement will also always be the same and your voice will fade as you speak your last words before losing consciousness, which in the mind of the assailant could be the prelude to death: "Look, I just got out of the hospital and am recovering from a heart attack, and I will do anything you say ... ."

At that point, roll your eyes up to the back of your head, grab your chest and collapse to the ground.

For just a moment, put yourself in the place of an abductor. You have just approached your intended victim as he or she begins to unlock the car door. You put a gun or knife to his side, telling him to get in the car or you will kill him. And he turns around and says, "I will do

anything you say, just don't hurt me, please. I just got out of the hospital and am recovering from a heart attack. Please just don't hurt ... ." And then the target hits the ground.

Now what? As I have found in my seminars, the results are always the same: Total panic by the assailant. First, the plan has obviously taken a turn for the worse. Second, if the abductor planned only to sexually assault, beat or rob and then release you, he now has to deal with perhaps having frightened you to death.

What you have accomplished is to make the assailant the "victim" of *your* "attack" by making him think you are either dead or close to death. The last thing a rapist, child molester or kidnapper needs is a dead body — one that is perhaps already attracting lots of attention from others nearby.

Before you scoff at that approach, try to think of a better and safer solution. I have found that this method is probably the safest defense against an abduction.

IF YOU AND THE ASSAILANT ARE IN YOUR CAR

The second situation I raised was an attempted abduction in which the assailant enters your car as you are parked or stopped at a traffic intersection. That represents a crime of opportunity. The crime can be prevented by always having your car doors locked, thus providing you with that all-important **one to five seconds** to escape. You are not going to have time to think about options in this case. You must already have a plan.

If the assailant enters the passenger side, whether he is armed or unarmed, your response will be the same as in the first situation. If you are at a convenience store, grocery store, shopping mall or traffic intersection, you must not leave the area. Buy some time and calm the assailant by assuring him you will do whatever he wants, and beg for mercy. Make him think he is in total control. Then carry out the "heart trouble" routine, this time collapsing on the steering column of the car. Coincidentally, hit your head on the steering column and make sure your arms just happen to become entangled in the wheel and on the horn.

Put yourself in the place of the assailant. What do you do? You can't very well move the intended victim over and get behind the wheel and drive. Are you going to shoot the victim? Probably not. First, the person may already be dead. Second, that would draw attention. While you are thinking about what to do, the horn is sounding nonstop, attracting lots of attention — the last thing you want. People are noticing the person slumped over the wheel and wondering why aren't you doing anything to aid the victim.

If you are in your car with the doors locked and windows up and find yourself facing an armed assailant demanding that you open the door, fainting on the steering column is effective. It attracts lots of attention when you fall on the horn, and causes a dilemma for the assailant. The chances he will shoot you are low, probably lower than if you were to try to drive away.

If the assailant opens the driver's door while you are parked and demands that you move over to the passenger side, your defense will vary only slightly. As always, your first response is the verbal counterattack of submission and weakness. But this time, rather than faint on the steering column, you faint and fall out of the car toward the assailant. This is even more effective if you fall so that you end up half in and half out of the car, making it extremely difficult for the assailant to even steal your car, since he had planned to use it to abduct you.

I recently conducted a seminar on this method of abduction prevention. As I approached the driver's side of the victim's car, which was parked in a row of cars, I jerked open the door and, pointing a gun at the woman, demanded that she move over quickly to the passenger side.

Instead the victim did exactly as taught, fainting and falling out of her car toward me. She was a large woman, which perhaps accounted for her falling much faster than I expected. Before I could move back, she had fallen on my foot and shin, pinning my leg under her chest, which caused me to fall back abruptly. Since I was between cars that were close together, I hit the back of my head on the car beside hers.

Regaining consciousness, I awoke to find myself trapped beneath the woman. I couldn't move back to get out from under her body

because I was wedged between the car behind me and the woman on top of me. It was quite a predicament. We all laughed later at how an assailant would have felt.

I have taught this method for many years and used the technique on many unsuspecting "assailants," and I have yet to meet one who could complete the abduction. If you doubt its effectiveness, test it with someone in a role-playing situation.

If the motor is running and your car is in gear, it is best to faint so that you are completely out of the car to avoid the possibility of being accidentally run over.

Your goal is to avoid a physical confrontation or struggle, thus greatly reducing your chances of injury at the hands of the assailant.

THE DRIVE-BY ABDUCTION

Probably the most common type of abduction occurs when the assailant pulls up and threatens or lures the victim into his vehicle.

This is the preferred method for many reasons. It affords better concealment of a weapon, offers a much quicker method of escape, whether the crime is successful or not, and reduces the chances of being identified by witnesses, because little if any of the criminal's physical characteristics are discernable if he remains in the vehicle.

Your choice of methods to escape an abduction increases slightly with this kind of crime. In a drive-by, there is a barrier between you and the assailant — his vehicle. His options are greatly reduced, along with his ability to complete an abduction, even when armed.

Yet this method of abduction is one of the most successful. If only all potential victims knew how easy it is to escape this threat, which is all the attempt really is.

A primary target of the drive-by abductor is children. A common ploy is to pull up next to a child walking to school or at play and ask for directions. Once the child is close enough, the abductor flashes a handgun and demands that the child get in the car. What happens next

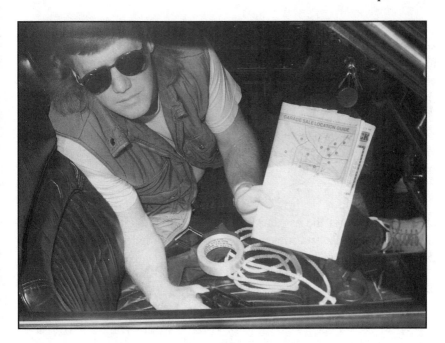

is all too familiar. We read almost daily about the murders and rapes of young children abducted in such a fashion.

DEFENSE AGAINST THE
DRIVE-BY ABDUCTOR

You must plan your course of action for the most common situations you might face in a drive-by abduction attempt.

The first situation arises when you are at least five to ten feet away from the abductor's car when threatened. Normally, the assailant will attempt to lure a victim closer by asking where someone lives, then pretending not to be able to hear the intended victim's response.

Another ploy is to brandish a map or newspaper and ask for directions. Or the abductor may pose as a law enforcement authority, complete with badge.

Obviously, you want to make sure you keep as much distance as possible between you and the assailant's car so you can't be grabbed

without forcing the abductor to leave his car — the last thing an abductor wants to do. An abductor will almost always abandon the attempt rather than have to physically force a victim into a vehicle. It is too easy to go find another victim who will get in the car when threatened.

Once it becomes clear that you are the target of an abductor and you have the luxury of several feet between you and the assailant's car, one of two methods should be used.

You guessed it. Faint. You rely on passive resistance because it is effective. What is the assailant going to do now? Get out of his car, walk over to an unconscious victim, try to pick him up, and lift him into the car? A criminal is going to get away as fast as he can and chalk that abduction attempt up to experience, especially if the incident occurs in a neighborhood or at a school where others are nearby.

What are passerbys going to do? What would you do if you saw someone faint on the sidewalk? Most would go to the aid of the person, especially a child or woman. The last thing an abductor wants to see, or be seen by, are witnesses who can identify him or his vehicle.

Most people wouldn't give a second thought to seeing a child or adult talking to someone in a car, walking over to the car, getting in and riding away. Not until later, at least, upon learning that the person was

forcefully abducted. Quite often, by that time the victim is dead.

Instead, if you faint, will the assailant shoot you? Realistically, the chances are remote. First, the attention such an action would generate is the last thing an abductor wants. He wants to quietly complete the crime attracting as little attention as possible.

Most abductors are habitual sex offenders or serial murderers, and their desires are not satisfied by just the act of killing the victim. In his mind, just shooting you does not "complete the crime."

And the abductor may not even have a firearm. He may use one of many lures, such as impersonation of a police officer by showing a badge. And even if the abductor is armed and wants to shoot, it is difficult now to see you, much less shoot you, if you have fainted to the ground. If you are within five to ten feet of the car when you faint, you have removed yourself from the line of sight and fire.

IF YOUR ASSAILANT
LEAVES HIS CAR

One possible result of fainting is that rarely, the abductor could get out of the car and attempt to pick you up and carry you to the car. That would happen only when you are isolated from others. Should that occur, then is the time to use the bicycle kick described in Tip 5. Stay on your back and kick, as though you are riding a bicycle, toward the vital areas I outlined in Tip 5. Kick toward the knees, eyes, groin and throat, yelling the entire time, "Leave me alone, I'm not going anywhere."

Or if you really want to get assistance yell, "Police officer needs assistance." If there is one thing that police respond to, it is another officer in trouble. If there is anyone nearby to hear, in a matter of seconds there will be police cars everywhere. Take the word of a former police officer. An officer might not like your using the method, but in a matter of life and death, do what you must to survive. The assailant might even abort the attempted abduction if he thinks he has accidentally picked a police officer as his victim.

RUN AWAY

Another method, when there is some distance between you and the abductor's car, is to simply run away. Your first response might be, but what if he shoots? My reply is, if he will shoot you in a mall parking lot or neighborhood, what will he do to you in an isolated area? Your chances of being shot are much less in a populated area. And you shouldn't just run away, you should run away intelligently.

Never run directly away from the car. If you are facing the passenger's or driver's side when confronted, and you opt against fainting, distance yourself from the car by running toward the rear of the car as you move away. That makes it next to impossible for the assailant to fire without blowing out the back window of his car. And if he is crazy enough to shoot, you are a much harder target to hit while running in that direction. Experiments I have conducted confirm this.

It is almost impossible to shoot someone running toward the rear of a car when you are in the driver's seat. You have to raise the gun over the passenger's seat to even get a decent aim at the intended target. And by then, the victim is well out of range.

Children are even better at escaping in such situations. Using the "duck-and-run" method I teach in my role-play seminars, children become an impossible target to see or hit. The chances an assailant will shoot are rare, and if he does he will be easy to identify later. Look for a car without a back window and broken glass all over the trunk.

Always run toward the rear of the car to make it difficult for the abductor to pursue you in the vehicle. Running toward the rear of the car also lessens the chance the assailant can use his car to injure you.

In all three situations I have just described, your solutions are simple and to the point. **Never Leave a Populated Area when Confronted by an Abductor.** When threatened, use passive resistance (fainting) rather than physical counteraction. If you somehow believe the tactic won't work, you still must not leave the public's view.

ANOTHER METHOD IF
YOU AND THE ASSAILANT
ARE IN YOUR CAR

When told to drive, you should, if nothing else, drive into the side of any car parked near yours. Or better yet, if you are at a mall, drive directly into the mall entrance, unless doing so would endanger others. Don't accelerate and hit the building at 30 miles an hour. But even if you do, that is better than leaving a populated area where people can help you. Just don't run over anyone.

What always attracts lots of people? An accident. People will swarm to a car that has just driven through the front door of a mall, wanting to see if anyone is injured. And a swarm of spectators wanting to help is the last thing an abductor wants to see.

If you are confronted while approaching or after exiting your car, your plan of action should be to "faint" using the methods outlined in this chapter. You can't wait until the attempted abduction occurs to think what to do. Go over in your mind at least monthly what you are going to do if confronted, and that will be the only alternative you will consider.

FOR YOUR CHILDREN

I recently tested a friend's four-year-old child to see how she would respond. Her parents had discussed the dangers posed by strangers offering money and toys to lure her into going with them, and they told her how the stranger really only wanted to get her away and hurt her. She had been told to always come inside if someone approached her on foot or in a car.

When I drove up, the girl was washing some seashells she had collected on vacation. Without getting out of my car, I asked what she was doing. She told me about her shells and continued to wash them with a water hose. I then asked her if she wanted to go riding for a few minutes. She shook her head and said "No," never looking up. I then

said, "Aw, come on, just for a few minutes, I'll bring you right back." "Nope," was her reply, still without looking up.

Again I used my ice cream lure and said, "How about we go get an ice cream cone and I will bring you right back." With that, she looked up, said "Okay," and started toward the car. The story has a happy ending only because it was a simulation.

If you apply no other tips in this book, please use this one. Ask your children or grandchildren what they would do if confronted by someone demanding that they go with them. Make sure you discuss the alternatives outlined in this chapter and why they must not go with a stranger. It is well worth the time to get a friend at work, or someone else your child would not know, to role-play an abduction attempt.

Take the time to make sure your child knows to never go with someone he doesn't know and is aware of all the lures that might be attempted to gain his confidence. Sadly, we must also discuss taking precautions even against family members. Don't forget, many children are molested by a family member.

By having a plan and teaching your children what to do in potential situations, you can save yourself and your children heartbreak.

EVEN MY OWN FAMILY

I once returned home from conducting an abduction prevention seminar for children and was discussing with my wife how successful the seminar had been.

One of my sons, who was ten at the time, overheard the conversation and inquired about the seminar. I had presumed that from years of having to listen to me sermonize about the dangers of crime in our society, he knew what to do if faced with the threat of abduction. Somehow, though, I had managed to teach everyone but my own children.

When I went into a role-play and pointed an empty pistol at him and asked what he would do if threatened and told to get in a car, the look of fear in his eyes told me, before he could say a word, what he

would do. Sheepishly, he replied, "Daddy, I guess I would get in the car." Needless to say, I immediately conducted a private seminar for my two sons. I can safely say now that there is no way either one will ever accompany an armed or unarmed abductor if confronted.

I am amazed at how children can learn in just a few hours to escape an attempted abduction. Make sure that you periodically reinforce these concepts with your children. We as adults are much more aware of the dangers we all face because of the rising epidemic of crime. We often avoid discussing these problems because we don't want to make our children paranoid or we don't think it can ever happen to our family.

HOW TO FALL
WHEN FAINTING

I'm sure by now many of you are convinced that fainting is a good choice when confronted by an assailant, but you are wondering how to faint without injuring yourself.

This book is intended to be a textbook for those attending my seminars and to be used for a reference when reviewing concepts presented in the seminars. For those not able to attend my seminars, I will explain the basics of fainting without injuring yourself.

Visualize two scenes. The first is a large tree falling and hitting the ground. Imagine the force at the first moment of contact with the ground: Quite a collision. Now, visualize a building being razed with explosives. The building essentially crumbles with no parts hitting the ground at the same time. It is almost as if the building just sits down.

It is a difficult concept to teach by visualizing, but when fainting, you must crumble slowly to the ground rather than fall like the tree. You accomplish that by bending your knees and slowly falling and twisting to one side, making sure you do not allow any particular area of the body to absorb all of the impact of striking the ground. If possible, to avoid serious injury, fall on one side, making sure not to land on your back or face.

Also, use your hands as you approach the ground to break your fall. That will serve to protect other, more vital parts from any damage. If you will visualize the concept of the crumbling building, it will help you to fall correctly. By falling on your side, you can position your head to land on your upper arm, if it is extended from your body. Use it as a cushion to prevent your head from striking the ground. Also, if you are between cars on a parking lot or near the door of a building, as you crumble, fall toward the car or door and use it to break your fall.

Once down, do not move. With any luck, you have landed on your side and have many of your vital organs protected, just in case the assailant decides to kick you for fainting.

It might seem silly, but it is wise to practice falling in your home on carpet or pillows if you think you might hesitate to faint because of the fear of falling. The injuries from fainting will be much less serious than the injuries likely if you accompany the assailant.

Another possible ploy is pretending to have a seizure, jerking your body violently to even further confuse the assailant. This is especially effective for children threatened with abduction in a mall or theater. It draws an immediate crowd of people wanting to see if they can help.

No matter which scheme you choose, do not look up to see if the assailant is still there. You must play out the role convincingly, even if it means the assailant escapes as others approach. Don't jump up and point out the assailant until you are absolutely sure there are others to assist you.

It might make it a little easier, if you still don't believe you could convincingly faint to avoid abduction, to think about the alternative.

OTHER SITUATIONS WHERE FAINTING MIGHT SAVE YOUR LIFE

MASS SHOOTINGS

People have used the ploy of playing dead to avoid being shot in many mass shootings.

In the Texas Tower massacre of 1968, in which a sniper killed many people on the University of Texas campus, several people survived by playing dead. There are many cases of soldiers who pretended to be dead when overrun by enemy troops and survived.

As this chapter was being written, the worst mass shooting in United States history occurred at a Killeen, Texas, restaurant. More than twenty people were killed as a man armed with a pistol randomly shot more than forty people in a fifteen-minute period before taking his own life. At least two people who escaped death credited their survival to pretending to have been shot and playing dead.

In such situations, the assailant is obviously a disturbed person who is neither rational nor predictable. That is why it is critical to already have a plan of action. Feigning death is a good option to consider for several reasons. It gets you out of the immediate line of fire. Most people want to instinctively run to escape — quite often a deadly choice. Most assailants in such incidents are responding to any stimuli with gunfire. Anything that moves is a potential target — and often is a target for no other reason.

The assailant thinks he has already shot you. In his agitated state of mind, he has no idea how many or whom he has already injured. These are terrible things to have to think about, but sadly, having a survival plan is a necessity for just this kind of situation.

The same kind of crime, committed by disgruntled employees and spurned lovers, is becoming common in the workplace. One never knows what will cause someone to finally "go over the edge" and commit such a crime. You need to have a plan for such a "disaster," just as you do for a fire or other life-threatening emergency.

What would or could you do if you were at work and someone entered and began randomly shooting? You must have already considered all options. Is an escape route available to leave the building without being seen? Is a room that can be locked and secured available to shelter employees? Is there time to use either of these two alternatives before being noticed by the assailant?

If neither of these is possible, then you must again consider the options of fainting or pretending to be dead. If you have already witnessed the assailant shooting anyone who moves, *¹ ₁ it is time to play dead, and it doesn't even matter if you fall like the tree we described earlier. Just get down and don't move. The natural reaction of most people will always be to run. You must overcome that instinct and decide how best to increase your chances of surviving. Quite often, playing opossum is a good choice.

WHEN YOU HAVE
NO OTHER OPTIONS

In Tip 1, I discussed how George Kent Wallace would impersonate a police detective and pick up teenage boys at malls "for questioning." He would cuff and shackle them, place them in his car and drive them to an isolated rural area. He was successful in using that ploy to abduct and murder several young men.

In my seminars, many times people ask how Wallace was caught. The only reason he was captured and convicted is the reaction of the last boy he abducted. The youth unknowingly followed two of the tips outlined in this book — the tip I am discussing now, Tip 9, how to avoid abduction, and Tip 1, outsmarting your assailant.

When Wallace pulled him out of the car and began choking him with a rope, instead of continuing to fight back, the boy played dead. Wallace then removed the restraints and left the boy unattended while he gathered weights to sink the body in a livestock pond. Once the boy felt there was a safe distance between him and his abductor, he jumped up and ran for his life until he finally stumbled onto a farmhouse.

The police were notified, and Wallace was quickly apprehended. Otherwise, he might still be abducting and killing. Who knows how many more just like him are operating today?

SUMMARY

Throughout this chapter, I have emphasized one particular defense against abduction and kidnapping; the use of passive resistance (fainting). As I have mentioned repeatedly throughout this book, no one solution can be guaranteed to work every time. Other books outline alternative self-protection measures that also may be effective. You must decide for yourself, after looking at all options, what you or a family member will do if ever faced with such a situation. The most important point to remember is, no matter what method of self-protection you choose to use in an abduction attempt,

GOING WITH AN ABDUCTOR IS NOT AN OPTION.

10

Tip 10

Use Positive Mental Survival Training

W ell, it finally happened to me. I had just gotten back in my car after filling it up with gas at a service station, when suddenly a man jerked open the passenger side door and jumped in. He immediately told me to drive. And then he exposed a knife, saying, "Get this car out of here now, or I'll kill you."

I went blank for just a few seconds, not knowing what to do. Then I remembered my DEFENSIVE LIVING Ten Tips and thought, I know what I am supposed to do, but can I really pull this off? Should I just pass out now on the steering column and start honking the horn, or should I drive through the front of the service station? I wish I had thought about this before now. I can't believe I left my car doors unlocked.

Fortunately for me, this was a "mental imaging" exercise I was experiencing, not the real thing. I had made the mistake of not locking

my car doors after getting in my car and decided to use the experience to role-play mentally what I would have done had someone jumped in the car with me.

Sound silly? If you think so, I will feel sorry if you experience an actual or attempted assault. I hate to say it, but if your only preparation for assault prevention is reading this book and deciding you are prepared to defend yourself, then as Jerry Clowers, the comedian, would say, "You in a heap 'a trouble, boy."

That is why I have included this chapter as one of the Ten Tips for assault prevention. If you don't practice and incorporate the previous nine Tips discussed by using **Tip 10, Use Positive Mental Survival Training**, then within a few months you will have forgotten most of what you have read in this book.

USE MENTAL IMAGING AND ROLE-PLAY

Mental imaging and role-play are two of the most practical ways to prepare for an actual threat of criminal victimization.

Simulation drills are used extensively in almost every kind of emergency preparedness exercise, from fire drills to tornado drills to mass evacuation exercises. Simulation exercises are an integral part of training in military preparedness, police hostage negotiations and corporate life. Many Fortune 500 companies use simulated work scenarios to determine a job applicant's ability to work under pressure.

Normally, in a dangerous or stressful situation, you don't have the time to think about alternatives and must rely on your instincts if you don't have the proper mental preparation. That is why it is so important to already have a stored program in your mind, a previously prepared response, which guides your actions.

Mental survival training is at least as important as any physical training you can undergo in preparing for the possibility of physical

assault. That is why I have included it as one of the Ten Tips in avoiding criminal victimization.

The nine Tips presented in the preceding chapters can have a great impact on reducing your chances of becoming the victim of personal assault, but only if you integrate them into your daily habits. That hinges on your ability to consciously review the Ten Tips and the situations that are addressed throughout the chapters. After picturing yourself in various threatening situations and mentally developing a response, eventually that response will become an unconscious but intelligently planned reaction.

If you have never thought about what you would do in a particular situation, how can you possibly expect to make a prudent decision that will keep you from being victimized? By now, you should have overcome the subconscious belief that you have no alternatives when faced with the possibility of violent assault.

The nervous system handles vividly imagined experiences as "real" happenings. That is why dreams sometimes seem so real. After "imaging" a particular experience several times, the brain and nervous system will store that experience, and when requested to repeat it, will respond accordingly. Just as you could memorize the physical steps in a marching drill through constant repetition of the moves, you can likewise memorize the mental steps involved in certain imagined assaults and program a safe response to them.

Occasionally picture situations like the one described at the beginning of this chapter, and think of your possible alternatives. Then select one or two that were outlined in the book or that you have developed yourself, and mentally role-play those options. See yourself successfully avoiding the confrontation through the use of your chosen defense.

Ask yourself periodically what you would do if ... . And "see" yourself reacting with an intelligent response.

A good time to practice mental imaging and role-play is when you

are driving. Rather than mindlessly daydreaming or worrying about other problems, develop your DEFENSIVE LIVING habits and review the Ten Tips for assault prevention.

This is also one of the easiest forms of self-defense to practice. Since you can develop good assault prevention skills by mentally planning your defense, these methods lend themselves well to use by those who are unable to develop a physical means of self-defense. You are not limited by your age, sex, physical disability or available time. Someone eighty years old can use the DEFENSIVE LIVING tips just as effectively as someone sixty years younger.

WEIGH THE COSTS

Most of the tips outlined cost no money to practice. This book offers an inexpensive yet effective method of avoiding criminal assault by installing your own alarm system in your mind.

- It costs nothing to make eye contact and speak to people, but that practice can help develop the confidence so important in ensuring that you **Do Not Think and Look Like a Victim — Tip 1**.

- It costs nothing to develop the habit of **Always Locking the Doors In Your Car or Home Immediately After Entering or Exiting.** Remember, your car or home can be a barrier or a trap, depending on your intelligently using them to protect you — **Tip 2**.

- It costs nothing to **Always Use the Buddy System**, but learning to always have other people around you or to use others can greatly reduce your chances of being victimized. Remember, strength in numbers — **Tip 3**.

- It costs nothing to **Take 15 to 30 Seconds to Observe Your Destination Area Before Approaching.** Those few seconds could save your life — **Tip 4**.

- It costs nothing but a little pride to **Not Physically Resist an Assailant, Except to Avoid Injury or Death**. Remember, material possessions can be replaced. Your life or your child's life can't — **Tip 5**.

- It costs little to equip yourself with several extremely effective self-protection weapons. **If You Are Going to Carry a Weapon, Know How to Use It and Have It Available — Tip 6**. Your best weapon, your intelligence, doesn't cost anything.

- It costs nothing to **Determine Safe Locations Available** should you be followed by a potential assailant while walking or driving — **Tip 7**.

- It costs nothing to **Become Aware of Crime Trends and Criminal Characteristics**. Remember, know the enemy and know yourself and you greatly increase your chances of survival — **Tip 8**.

- It costs nothing to "faint" or play dead, and that is what you must do to make sure you **Never Leave a Public Area With An Abductor**. Remember, once out of the public eye, you are at your assailant's mercy — **Tip 9**.

- It costs nothing to periodically review these DEFENSIVE LIVING tips and **Use Positive Mental Survival Training** and role-play successful solutions, which can greatly reduce your chances of becoming a crime victim — **Tip 10**.

All of these DEFENSIVE LIVING tips can be developed without spending hundreds of dollars on faddish assault prevention programs. When a self-protection weapon is desired, I pointed out several inexpensive ones in Tip 6, such as a highway flare that can be purchased for about $2 or a can of pepper spray (OC) that sells for about $15. Both are effective against animal and human predators.

Except for the cost of this book, your only investment is to make a

conscious decision to begin to incorporate these Ten Tips into your daily habits. Each of my Ten Tips can be summarized in one brief paragraph. Memorize it, and repeat it periodically. It will enable you to become much more confident in all aspects of life.

"Those who excel at resolving difficulties do so before they arise. For to win 100 victories in 100 battles is not the acme of skill. To defeat the enemy without fighting is the acme of skill."

Sun Tzu, *The Art of War*, 400 B.C.

Section III

Summary

I now understand why a movie takes so long to produce and why so much of it ends up on the cutting-room floor.

I also have a much greater respect for those who write and edit books as their chosen profession. I never dreamed of how difficult it could be to transfer my thoughts from the spoken to the written word.

Now that I have completed my first book, I am both elated and sad. Elated because the book is finally finished, after years of planning and persevering. Sad because it is drawing to a close and I will miss the late nights spent with only my thoughts and my computer.

Writing this book has given me the opportunity to learn so much about victims of personal crimes. I have also learned much about myself. I hope you can benefit as much from reading this book as I have from writing it. I am grateful to all who have shared their experiences with me. I have learned more, and continue to learn more each day, from my seminar participants than I can ever teach.

The motto for the American Society of Law Enforcement Trainers, of which I am a member, is the Latin phrase "Qui Docet, Discet," which translated means, "He Who Teaches, Learns." I couldn't express my sentiments better.

If I have offended anyone with the stories or concepts presented, it was inadvertent. My only intention was, and continues to be, to share the knowledge I have been exposed to the last thirty years in teaching and training in the field of self-protection.

SELF-DEFENSE "EXPERT"

I always encounter a few raised eyebrows when I introduce myself as an assault prevention expert. That is, until I define what I consider an expert to be. My definition of an expert in any field is "one who finally knows enough about a subject to realize how much he really doesn't know and how much is left to learn."

A very dear friend and fellow martial artist, Ernest "Mike" Mika, a legitimate judo expert, once tried to explain to me through a story what a real expert in the martial arts is. At the time, I was a twenty-one-year-old self-professed self-defense expert, and the story fell on deaf ears.

He shared with me the history of the belt ranking structure in the Japanese martial arts system. At the age of twenty-one, I failed to comprehend his analogy. Now, after teaching self-defense for those twenty-five years, I finally realize what he was attempting to tell me.

When you begin the study of karate or judo, the first belt you are awarded is the white belt. It represents the purity and innocence of a newborn child. You come into the world with no knowledge and depend on others for your survival and guidance.

As you grow and continue to learn, you progress to the coveted rank of 1st Degree black belt. Now you become dangerous, because you really think you do know something about the martial arts.

As you progress through the higher degrees of black belt, your confidence and knowledge continue to expand. At the 5th Degree of black belt, which is the master level, you are certain you are a legitimate expert in the martial arts.

Then, as if you cross some imaginary line, at the 6th and 7th Degrees of black belt you begin to realize how much there is that you don't know, and what you thought you knew is much more complex than you ever realized.

By the time you reach the 8th and 9th Degree levels of black belt, you have accepted the fact that you will never be able to learn all there

is to know in the martial arts. You realize that as your knowledge has grown, so has the amount of information available to be learned.

Then finally, after a minimum of fifty years of study in the martial arts, you are qualified to wear the highest rank attainable: The WHITE belt! The 10th Degree of black belt is denoted by the wearing of a solid white belt, rather than the traditional black belt.

It signifies the lifelong quest for knowledge and the humbleness that one must return to, just like a newborn. For only with old age and the wisdom that accompanies it do you finally realize that what is important is not how much you know, but that you realize how much you don't know and how much knowledge there is still to be learned from others around you.

Thank you Mika-San (most honorable) for making me an expert in the study of life, and a special thanks to all of my students. You have taught me more than I could ever teach you. I am grateful to all of you for helping me to learn more about myself.

Bo Hardy
March 1992

NOTES

FROM YOUR
TAIHO-RYU FAMILY

After I entered martial arts training, Bo Hardy soon became my role model, then my mentor, and has since become one of my closest friends. Thank you, Sensei, for your kindness, compassion and concern and the "direction" you have provided me and many, many others.

Richard D. Smith
Dallas/Ft. Worth, Texas

Acknowledgements

I have many people to thank for assisting me in the completion of my first book, *DEFENSIVE LIVING, When Defensive Driving, Diets and Exercise Aren't Enough to Keep You Alive and Well!* Some of you have been directly involved throughout the entire project. Others have lent your support as needed. I am grateful to all of you for the encouragement and assistance you have provided.

First, to my wife, **Mindy**, and sons, **Bo** and **Matt**; thanks for putting up with me and trying to understand what keeps me in high gear twenty hours a day. I'm still waiting on the T-shirt reading "**REST STRESSES ME OUT!**" you are going to have made for me. It really does fit me perfectly.

To **Richard D. Smith**, who has been instrumental in the development of DEFENSIVE LIVING™ INC. and this book; without your untiring effort and suggestions, the book would still not be finished. Having been a martial arts student of mine for the past eighteen years, you seem to always know exactly what I am thinking. Your assistance in the creative design of this book has made it much more readable. Thank you for your interest and dedication. We both have learned more from writing this book than we can ever teach anyone. Now let's get started on the next two!

To **Ed Gray**, my editor; thank you for your expertise and patience. Your skills and knowledge made me realize I am a "white belt" beginner in the art of writing and you are a true master. Thanks for being so diplomatic when I insisted on including my funny little puns. You are a true professional.

To **Nelson Hodges**, owner of Nelson Hodges Architects and a black belt student of mine; thank you for providing Richard Smith with extensive time and equipment to edit content and format and design this book when he could have been working on architecture projects.

Thanks also to all of the **DEFENSIVE LIVING™ INC. staff** for believing so strongly in the material and for your effort to help others avoid victimization.

To **Pamela Pruett Power**, who provided the photographs for the book; taking the pictures was one of the most enjoyable parts in completing this book.

To **Karen** and **Kevin Rutherford, Johnny Brown, Sam Power, Russell Love, Mindy** and **Matt Hardy** and **Richard Smith**; thanks for being the models for the pictures. You guys are really Hollywood material!

A THANKS TO THOSE WHO WERE AND STILL ARE AN INSPIRATION TO ME, BUT MAY NOT KNOW IT

To **John Atkinson**; what can I say? You have always been there for me when I needed encouragement. You taught me that anyone can do anything if he is just willing to work for it. When my family literally didn't know where the next $10 was coming from, you always had a way for us to make ends meet. You taught me how to silk-screen, build trophies and paint signs, just to name a few things. But most importantly, you taught me the value of true friendship. I will forever be indebted to you. Thank you.

To **Walter Jennings**; you unknowingly are probably more responsible for my finishing this book than anyone else. Every time I would quit working on it, you would bring me another one of those blasted "motivational" books or send me to a motivational seminar. Believe it or not, Walter, I read those books, and guess what? They all said the same thing — "The only difference between successful and unsuccessful people is that the successful ones do what the unsuccessful don't or won't do!" Thanks, Walter.

To my **friends and co-workers** at Southwestern Bell; thanks for the friendship and the interest in my book. Thanks also for helping me realize that life is too short to be taken too seriously.

To my **Taiho-Ryu "family"**; thank you for your dedication to the principles that Taiho-Ryu is founded on: Discipline, honor, respect and humility. If everyone would adopt these values, I wouldn't be writing books on assault prevention.

In memory of my mother, **Anna Marie Hardy**; thank you for teaching me that an education is the most valuable possession any person can obtain. Although we were very poor financially, Pee Wee (my sister) and I learned from you that anyone can overcome adversity with an education and family to depend on when you need them.

To **Pee Wee Hardy** and **Aunt Thresa Failla**, who had to fill in for my mother since she had to work double shifts all of her life for us to just get by; thank you both. You were excellent at that job.

To **Uncle "Satch" Failla** and **Uncle Bobby Joe Goodman**; you always took the time to include me in the outings with your boys. Thank you.

To all of my **family**; I can never repay the kindness you have shown me. Thank you all.

Bo Hardy

Table of Contents

DEFENSIVE LIVING
When Defensive Driving, Diets and Exercise Aren't Enough to Keep You Alive and Well!

Contents

Section I

Section II

Tip 2
**Always Lock the Doors In Your
Car and Home Immediately
After Entering or Exiting**
Page 58

Tip 3
Always Use the Buddy System
Page 78

Tip 4
**Take 15 to 30 Seconds
to Observe Your Destination
Area Before Approaching**
Page 94

Tip 5
**If You Decide to Physically
Resist Your Assailant,
Do So Only to Avoid
Personal Injury or Death**
Page 104

Tip 6
**If You Are Going to Carry
a Weapon, Know How to
Use It and Have It Available**
Page 126

Tip 7
**Determine Safe Locations
Available 24 Hours a Day
In Your City and On
Frequently Traveled Routes**
Page 168

Section III

Section I

You May Have One
to Five Seconds ...

It is Wednesday afternoon, about 1:30.

You are walking to your car after shopping at the local mall. You unlock the car door. You begin to get in and from seemingly nowhere a very calm but aggressive voice says, "Get in the car and move over to the passenger side or I'll kill you!" Quickly turning and seeing your assailant, you are gripped by fear as a knife is pressed to your ribs. What do you do?

Your child is in the front yard of your residence. A man pulls up in a vehicle and asks for directions. Walking up to the passenger door of the vehicle, your child notices the man has a gun in his hand. The gun is pointed directly at your child. The man very firmly states, "Get in the car or I'll kill you!" What would your child do?

You, or your child, may have **one to five seconds** to make one of the most important decisions of your life.

How This Book Is Different From Other Self-Defense Books

Defensive LIVING emphasizes common-sense approaches to many kinds of assaults that often change a victim's life forever. It offers ways of avoiding crimes that are often crimes of opportunity simply because the victims, out of habit, made themselves available to be victimized.

Ten years ago, most people would claim that abduction was so rare it could never happen to them or their child.

I have found in my seminars that more and more people no longer assume they are immune from becoming the victim of an attack such as those abduction situations. They have come to live with the fear of being attacked or kidnapped. They worry about it happening to themselves as well as to their children, spouse or some other relative.

Sadly, these incidents happen every day, in every corner of the United States. Even more sad is the fact that many of the victims are subsequently beaten, raped, murdered and often never heard from again. Often there is a safe, practical defense against abduction.

What of those people who believe they can't become a crime victim? When it happens, they say, "I can't believe this happened to our family! Our lives will never be the same!"

DEDICATION

For some, reading this book will be difficult. They are among those who have already become the victim of a violent assault or have been victimized to a degree that changed their lives dramatically.

For others, the fear of assault has driven them to change their lifestyles. And then there are those who, oblivious to the world around them, don't even realize that crime exists and somehow, by the grace of God, have not been victimized.

This book is dedicated to all the victims of crime who just didn't know that there were alternatives to becoming a victim.

In Michigan, to the ten-year-old boy who went to the restroom at a movie theater and was never seen alive again. His body was found two weeks later in a wooded area.

In Texas, to the fourteen-year-old girl who was abducted as she walked to school. Her body was recovered two days later at a city dump. She had been sexually assaulted and strangled.

In New York, to the fifty-year-old woman who was pushed to her death in front of a subway because she wouldn't relinquish her purse to an attacker. She had one dollar in her purse.

In Fort Worth, to the two women who were abducted from their business by two assailants who drove them around for hours and raped and beat them. One of the victims was left in an abandoned house with her head wrapped in duct tape and she suffocated. The other victim survived, but will never be the same.

In Arkansas, to the schoolteacher who was forced at knifepoint into a vehicle and later found sexually assaulted, beaten and with her throat slit.

In New Jersey, to the woman who was sitting in her unlocked car waiting for her college class to begin. She was abducted and raped. She has revealed in several national magazines how her life changed after that day and all the suffering, both physical and mental, she and her family still endure years later.

In California, to the eighty-year-old woman who would not give up her purse to an assailant. She was dragged several yards and then shot three times in the abdomen. She spent two weeks in a hospital and incurred thousands of dollars in medical bills. She had $13 in her purse.

In Florida, to the forty-year-old executive of a large corporation. He was abducted at knifepoint for ransom. His body was found three days later after the two million dollar ransom had been paid.

Incidents like these happen every day and quite often can be avoided by simply following my Ten Tips. A big part of the battle against personal crime is knowing that there are steps you can take to lessen your chances of becoming a victim.

This book can help anyone concerned with the threat of violent crime. It includes information that will benefit the executive, the husband, the wife and the child. It does not include hundreds of tips, as many self-defense books do. That's because when presented with too much information, most people will read the material, realize they can't possibly remember all the intricate details, and wind up not taking any of the suggestions seriously.

This book will not teach you how to "rip an assailant's heart out and show it to him before he dies." What DEFENSIVE LIVING does do is provide ten, and only ten, important tips that if followed will greatly reduce your chance of becoming a victim of assault, abduction and other serious crimes.

THE TEACHINGS OF
MOTHER NATURE

Many animals aren't as fortunate as those who have the natural weapons that the tiger, the wild boar or the snake do. They have to rely on the buddy system to try to survive.

The giraffe travels in groups, as do zebra and gazelle, for protection from predators. There is an instinct to group together to protect the defenseless young and old animals. The animal predator, even when much stronger, will usually try to single out a victim, much as human predators do. Both human and animal predators will select as their primary target a victim who has strayed from the group, or a young victim who is slower and less wise to the dangers or an old or injured prey.

Isn't it interesting to note how the human predator stalks his prey in much the same way the animal predator does?

Many books on assault prevention mention some of my Ten Tips in DEFENSIVE LIVING. For example, **Tip 3, Always Use the Buddy System,** is one that everyone has heard. But what other books don't do is to detail how or why the tip is so important. When you understand that, for instance, more than ninety percent of sexual assaults involve one attacker and one victim, the concept of the buddy system takes on much greater importance.

Many of my DEFENSIVE LIVING tips come straight from nature. Much can be learned by studying how other creatures survive nature's never-ending attempt to make us all extinct. God has given all species unique ways to survive. For instance, the porcupine has its quills, the skunk has its repugnant spray, and the opossum somehow knows to play dead when threatened by an aggressor. You will learn to use similar weapons in later chapters. Fortunately, God has given you a brain to study these ways of nature as your primary weapon.

Each of the Ten Tips in DEFENSIVE LIVING largely involves using your brain to outsmart or trick your assailant. When physical action is required, a practical approach to the advantages and disadvantages of taking a certain course of action is discussed.

Animals instinctively use the weapons available to them. The most important point to remember as you read this book is to learn to use the most effective weapon we all possess — our brain.

These Ten Tips can help you and your family avoid becoming a victim of abduction, robbery and rape. Many of the tips will also enable you to develop a sense of confidence in other areas of your life. Once you begin to live these tips daily, you will be pleased with your increased sense of security.

I hope you find my Ten Tips informative and useful, whether you are an executive concerned about abduction, a parent who lives with the fear of a child being abducted or sexually assaulted, or even a 5th Degree black belt in karate who wants to begin teaching real self-defense.

After you read this book, I hope there is no way you or your child will ever get in a car with an assailant when lured or threatened with death or bodily harm.

If this book saves one life, and I know it will, then my effort will have been worthwhile.

Why You Must Read This Book

Arriving home from grocery shopping, the young woman noticed the clean-cut man, dressed in jeans and a windbreaker, walking away from her house. As she pulled into the driveway, he turned, smiled at her and began approaching. "Hi, I came by to see the stereo equipment you advertised in the paper," he said. "Have you sold it yet?"

She and her husband had received only a few telephone inquiries from their ad. "No, but it's in great shape," she replied as he helped her carry the groceries to the front door. Once inside, she told the young man that she should call her husband to find out which of the stereo pieces were for sale and the exact amount he wanted for each.

As she was talking to her husband, she did not pay much attention to the visitor, who was looking at the family pictures hanging on the wall. She hung up the telephone and turned toward the stranger. He was facing her with a gun in his right hand and was pulling a roll of rope from his jacket. "Look, this is a robbery. Don't make it a murder. Just do as I say," he said, the pleasant smile no longer on his face.

5 OUT OF 6 PEOPLE WILL BE THE VICTIM OF ...

There are several reasons for you to take seriously the possibility of becoming the victim of assault. The first and foremost is that your chances of being physically assaulted are very high. According to the National Victim Center in Fort Worth, Texas, 83 percent of the population, or five out of six people, will be the victim of violent assault or attempted violent assault! According to federal government statistics, one out of three women will be sexually assaulted by the age of 45. For these statistics to be truly appreciated, you have only to look at two other deadly menaces.

Your chances of contracting some form of cancer in your lifetime are one in three, or 33 percent. Your chances of developing a form of heart disease are one in two, or 50 percent. Incredibly, your chances of becoming the victim of a violent assault are greater than those of developing either cancer or heart disease!

The good news is we are making great strides in finding solutions for cancer and heart disease and increasing our chances of surviving these two killers. The bad news is we spend little time or money developing "cures" for an equal threat to our well-being — violent assault. And unlike other "diseases," your chances of "contracting" this disease seem to be increasing, rather than decreasing. A job study revealed that one of the fastest-growing occupations over the next decade will be the correctional institution officer.

THE SCARS REMAIN

After he bound and raped the woman on the living room floor, the assailant rolled her in a rug, demanding to know where the money and jewelry were kept. Each time that she told him there was none, he grew angry, yelled obscenities and pointed the gun at her head. She was so sure she was going to be shot that each time she would close her eyes and tuck her head onto her shoulder and wait. Her rapist would threaten to shoot, then walk away. About half an hour after she had let him in, he threatened, "If I see you in court, I'll kill you!" He then took the keys to her car and drove away.

The physical and mental scars from an assault often remain long after the actual incident — if you are lucky enough to survive. Post-Traumatic Stress Disorder, an emotional trauma often associated with a violent assault, has been known to linger for the rest of some victims' lives.

Mental aftershocks include vivid flashbacks and nightmares. Long after an attack, a person resembling the attacker or the scent of a particular cologne can trigger a flashback so intense that the survivor believes the assault is happening again.

In some severe cases, long-term psychological damage results in fear, guilt, anxiety, depression, low self-esteem, and suicide attempts. Even though many victims learn to cope, no one is ever the same, especially in the case of rape. Some studies even show that sixteen percent of women who have been raped still suffer from Post-Traumatic Stress Disorder seventeen years later.

YOUR ENTIRE FAMILY IS VICTIMIZED

Once her rapist had left, the woman was able to loosen her bonds enough to hop across the street to a neighbor for help. The police and medical help soon arrived. After a medical and evidence-gathering exam, she was able to identify her assailant in a photo lineup. An arrest warrant was issued for the ex-convict and a bulletin was filed for her stolen car. Reports the next day, on television and in the papers, described the incident.

Six months later, her car was found abandoned in another state some 3,000 miles away. It had an additional 47,000 miles on the odometer since she had last driven it. Eventually, the repeat offender was arrested and brought to trial.

The first trial ended on a Friday. The woman felt that the city attorney's office had not been aggressive in trying her case, leaving out several key facts and pieces of evidence. After the jury had deliberated for an hour without reaching a verdict, the judge hastily declared a mistrial. She sat horrified as her assailant walked out of the courtroom and onto the streets.

By the end of the second trial, two years had passed since the incident occurred. The jury found the robber/rapist guilty and sentenced the multiple offender to the state's maximum sentence of forty years. However, under sentencing guidelines, he will be eligible for parole in sixteen years.

Not only the victim suffers when an assault or abduction occurs. The mental stress associated with being assaulted, or having a child or loved one abducted, can be overwhelming.

It becomes difficult to make decisions and to trust others, as well as oneself. It may become impossible to maintain any long-term intimate relationships. Many marriages break up after the spouse is sexually assaulted. Most people are devastated by a perceived loss of control and the knowledge that someone else can choose at any time to take control and have you do what they want you to do.

The inconvenience of medical care, hospital expenses, lost wages and time away from work for recovery, counseling or legal proceedings are just a few more reasons for avoiding assault. In a sense, DEFENSIVE LIVING is a form of insurance for you and your family.

If you are not concerned for your own personal safety, you owe it to your children to make them aware of the assault prevention concepts in this book. I have included a great deal of information devoted to children's safety and the avoidance of abduction. If for no other reason, read this book and ask your children what they would do if ...

Just as many of us have changed our eating habits to live healthier, more productive lives, we must change our living habits to prolong our lives and avoid this dreaded "disease" of assault. We spend time and money on exercise programs to improve our physical and cardiovascular condition. We can't afford to neglect an area just as important to our well-being.

My following DEFENSIVE LIVING Ten Tips can and will make a great difference in your chances of becoming a victim of assault. All you have to do is use them — every day! As with any habit, once they become stored in your mind, you will automatically begin to follow these safety rules without having to think.

Section II

1

Tip 1

Don't Think and Look Like a Victim

A man was moving his family from a New England state to Texas. After he had been laid off and out of work for nearly a year, his sister in Houston had helped him land a job.

He loaded his family and all their possessions into and on top of their station wagon and headed for a better life. After traveling for two days, they stopped in Dallas for dinner at a fast food restaurant before undertaking the last leg of their journey, only four more hours to Houston.

As the family approached their car after eating, two young men engaged them on the parking lot. The two had observed the family station wagon with out of state plates and the many items strapped to its roof. They knew the travelers were most likely just passing through and would have difficulty returning to Dallas to work with authorities investigating a crime.

One of the two pulled a revolver and demanded the father's wallet. When he refused, he was shot three times in the chest. The two criminals ran, leaving the man lying on the asphalt, where he died while his family watched.

WHY?

Numerous studies have been conducted to determine why an assailant chooses a particular victim. Leading universities, government agencies and experts in criminal psychology have spent millions of dollars and thousands of hours to find out why a total stranger attacks another total stranger.

I once watched several prison inmates, incarcerated for violent personal crimes, being interviewed on television. One particularly astute "street criminal" summed up all the studies succinctly. He bragged that he doesn't have a doctorate in psychology, a master's in sociology, or even a bachelor's degree in physical education, but he can pick a victim out of a hundred people in about three seconds! He didn't really know what particular characteristics made these people appear to be easy prey, just that they looked like easy victims.

Could it possibly be that simple? A criminal can just look at someone and decide if he or she is an easy target just waiting to be victimized? Yes, if you have been at it as long as some criminals have.

There are many things you can do to greatly reduce your chances of being victimized. Through awareness of what an assailant looks for in a victim, you can avoid many of the situations that make you vulnerable and you can take the appropriate action to escape becoming a victim.

This first tip sounds simple, but it is the most important and complex of all my Ten Tips to follow.

DON'T THINK AND LOOK LIKE A VICTIM

An elderly woman, walking to her car from shopping, was victimized by a purse snatcher. As the thief ran by the woman and grabbed her purse, she instinctively clung to it and began to battle for possession. After being dragged several feet by him, she continued to hold on to what was rightfully hers. The thief, realizing the woman was not going to give up her purse, decided he had struck it rich. Why else would she be resisting so intensely? He pulled out a pistol and shot the woman three times in the abdomen.

After several days in a hospital, thousands of dollars in medical bills and weeks of convalescence, the woman recovered. When it was later determined that the thief escaped with only $13, the woman was asked why on earth she resisted. Her proud reply was, "I never have and never will let anyone get the best of me!" Whether the woman will ever realize it, the thief obviously did get the best of her.

Most people already fall into one of two categories of victimization. You unconsciously possess many of the characteristics that make you either a prime candidate to be victimized or a prime candidate to avoid being victimized. Those characteristics include traits that are based not only on how you look, but also on how you think.

What is an assailant looking for in a victim, as far as mental characteristics? Someone who appears timid, afraid and looks like a victim, because he believes such a person also thinks like a victim. Predators seek the weak and avoid the strong — not only the physically strong but the mentally strong.

For those of you who possess the favorable characteristics, congratulations. Not only your good fortune has prevented you from becoming a victim of crime. For those of you who possess the unfavorable characteristics, good luck! Either you have already been the victim of a crime or you are a victim waiting for a crime to happen.

No matter which of the two categories you now fall into, this book contains principles that, if integrated into your daily habits, will greatly reduce your chances of becoming a crime victim. They will also enable you to feel better about yourself, develop self-confidence and have a sense of security you have perhaps never had.

That woman who refused to give up her purse reacted to her assault just as most people would. She based her response on two primary factors. Her instinctive impulse to resist was based on the first factor, her personality. The second factor that contributed to her injuries was her lack of knowledge of the correct action to take.

Unless you have the knowledge to do otherwise, your first response to an assault is going to be inherent in your personality. What you must learn by studying my Ten Tips is to let your intelligence, not your personality, guide your actions.

DON'T THINK LIKE A VICTIM

Sun Tzu, the noted Chinese writer and philosopher, discusses in his classic book, *The Art of War*, the two most important characteristics a soldier should possess to win in combat. If your troops are superior in morality and intelligence, then you are most assured of victory in any form of confrontation.

Whether you realize it or not, you are in combat every day. You deal with business customers, co-workers, family members and even yourself in a form of mental combat. Whether the battle involves two armies of powerful nations in actual military combat or only two people in a verbal confrontation, the same concepts apply to winning.

Sun Tzu believed that superior troop strength and superior firepower play an integral role in defeating an opponent. But more important than either of these are two other elements that, if exercised, will always lead to victory.

MORALITY

Your first step to avoid becoming a victim of assault is to develop morality. By morality, I mean having a strong belief in a principle and willingness to defend that principle at whatever cost. As a law-abiding citizen, you have a right to be left alone! If you want to walk down the street at ten at night alone, you should have the right to do so without fearing for your safety. Realistically, we know that isn't the case any longer, but it is important that we still believe we have that right.

In World War II, the Japanese military strategy was founded on one primary concept—morality. They believed in their destiny so intensely that if an individual soldier showed any form of cowardice, he was expected to commit suicide for having disgraced his family and country. There are documented accounts of Japanese soldiers who were discovered hiding in the jungles of Pacific Island countries, refusing to surrender or accept defeat some fifty years later.

Twenty years after World War II, the Vietnam conflict offers a sobering example of what happens when a nation or individual doesn't know or believe in what they are fighting for. The purpose of this analogy is not to cast aspersion on any of our patriotic veterans who fought in the Vietnam War, but solely to show what happens when an army or individual does not believe in the cause they are fighting for. Our troops were thrown into a battle in which there was intense disagreement among citizens and troops alike about what our objectives were.

At the time, Sun Tzu follower Lieutenant Norman Schwarzkopf was so disgusted with the military and political infighting that he openly criticized the U.S. command. The war was fought without morality or intelligence, the two most important characteristics needed to achieve success, and the results would have been predictable for General Sun Tzu.

Twenty years after the Vietnam War, we finally see the principles of morality and intelligence applied to combat. In the war against Iraq, it was obvious that our military leaders, and President Bush, had learned a valuable lesson from reading *The Art of War*. In fact, the book was required reading for all military officers and encouraged reading for all troops.

The principles of morality and intelligence were applied to perfection. The results speak for themselves. It was critical that the population, the military, and the Arab world support the decision to engage Iraq militarily. By educating all of the need to stop Iraq's military buildup and protect resources, President Bush was successful beyond anyone's dreams in gaining moral support for military action. Not since World War II had there been such belief in a cause.

Our military leaders, including Commanding General Schwarzkopf, then applied the second principle, intelligence, to perfection. The systematic deployment of massive troop strength and sophisticated weaponry to the Saudi/Kuwait arena was so overwhelming, we had morally defeated the Iraqi forces before firing the first shot.

How would you have felt as an Iraqi soldier forced to the front lines, watching for months the enormous military buildup you were about to face. Do you think he perhaps had a feeling similar to one General George Custer had at the Little Big Horn?

BELIEVE IN WHAT YOU ARE FIGHTING FOR

If someone comes to your door or calls on the telephone attempting to sell some product, you shouldn't feel obligated to invite him in or listen to his sales pitch if you are not interested. Believing that you have the right to be left alone and not thinking of yourself as a victim are just as important as the physical characteristics you must develop to not look like a victim.

The assailant isn't always a stranger. Often in cases of date rape and incest or molestation, the assailant has already determined that his victim is timid or easily influenced. Don't ever accept being made a victim by a "friend."

Children must be taught to believe in a cause. They will be the targets of many forms of victimization, from an early age until they are wise enough to defend themselves. Not only do they risk being physically victimized, but they will encounter mental victimization at school by peers and by adults who will greatly influence their personalities. Such victimization, when a sense of self-worth and morality is absent, will affect a child's concept of himself and could leave a permanent scar on a child's mental health.

Developing morality not only concerns how you respond to others, but also how you view your own self-worth. My modern-day Sun Tzu of the business world, the late Sam Walton, founder of Wal-Mart, summed up the importance of morality when he stated:

"The winners of the world are not easily intimidated."

Believing in yourself is not only the first step in not becoming a crime victim, but also the first step in achieving any goal.

INTELLIGENCE

"Those who excel at resolving difficulties do so before they arise. For to win one hundred victories in one hundred battles is not the acme of skill. To defeat the enemy without fighting is the true acme of skill."

Sun Tzu, *The Art of War*

The second and most important step to avoid thinking like a victim is to use your intelligence. Believing in your right to be left alone is important, but you must also defend yourself intelligently. The woman who wouldn't give up her purse did not fight an intelligent battle. She violated several of my Ten Tips. When I read about victimization, the majority of the victims violated at least one of my Ten Tips.

Not only should you use your intelligence to not think like a victim, everything you do to not look like a victim will hinge on outsmarting your assailant. Use methods that trick or confuse the assailant into thinking you are not what he is looking for.

To look confident, you must be confident, and the only way to develop real confidence is through knowledge.

You must have a plan of action before an attack occurs. It is too late to think what to do when a confrontation is imminent. If you decide to take physical counteraction, you must already have determined the advantages and disadvantages of the safest course. In most assaults, you will have little if any time to prepare, so planning a course of action is critical for survival or success.

Most assailants have a plan and quite often use methods of trickery and surprise to complete their crimes. You must have a superior plan. Everything you do to avoid becoming a crime victim will be based on your intelligence. Effectively using your intelligence will decrease your chances of becoming a victim.

DON'T LOOK LIKE A VICTIM

It is late at night. You are walking alone to your car after shopping at the mall. As you approach your car, a man gets out of the car beside yours and starts to walk toward you. It is obvious from his clothing and demeanor that he is not a representative from the Chamber of Commerce Welcome Wagon Committee. He says nothing as he approaches. When you are ten to twelve feet from your car, he positions himself between you and your car door. You have a feeling you are about to become the victim of a violent assault. What do you do?

At first, you might think that you should wait and see what happens. Or perhaps you should turn and run. If this person intends to assault you, those are the two things you can least afford to do.

How you react, both verbally and nonverbally, in those first seconds can greatly affect the outcome of the incident. There are several ways for you to outsmart an assailant so he will not see you as a victim and will choose someone else.

In this book, when I say go into action, I don't necessarily mean physical action. There are many ways to defeat a potential assailant without resorting to physical means. As Sun Tzu stated, your ultimate goal is to defeat the enemy without fighting.

PREDATOR/PREY

The first **one to five seconds** of an encounter with a possible assailant is the most important time, because the assailant is evaluating whether you qualify as a victim. Most assailants want to pick the easiest victim they can find. They are looking for a prey who won't resist.

Animal predators seek their prey similarly. Most predators will seek the weakest victim to ensure success. The weaker the opponent, the less energy expended to win the battle. If you have ever watched nature programs on television, you will see that principle in the animal kingdom. Just like human predators, they look for the easiest prey available.

HOW TO NOT
LOOK LIKE A VICTIM

It is often said that a person gets only one chance to make a first impression. At no time is that more important than when you are faced with the possibility of being physically assaulted.

There are several traits you can develop to improve your first impression and decrease your chance of being victimized. They range from the way you are physically built to what you say (which reflects your personality and can involve verbal role-playing) to how you dress (visual role-playing).

PHYSICAL CHARACTERISTICS

George Kent Wallace received the death penalty for killing several teenage boys. Following a well-developed plan, he would go to a shopping mall or grocery store and await a lone victim. He always picked teenage boys who were small and slightly built for their age.

He would impersonate a plainclothes police detective from another state and tell his victim they were wanted for questioning in a series of robberies in the adjacent state. The victims then allowed Wallace to restrain them with both handcuffs and leg shackles and place them in the back seat of his car. They were then driven to an isolated rural area, where they were strangled and their weighted body thrown into a livestock pond.

In describing how he selected his victims, he was simple and to the point. "I would always select a young teenage boy who looked like he wouldn't resist me."

Your actual physical characteristics — how you look — play a major role in determining your chances of being targeted as an assault victim. Do you appear confident, outgoing, sure of yourself, or do you appear timid, nervous and unsure of yourself? We can all think of people we know who fit either of those roles. You will often find that those who exhibit the timid, insecure personalities are often the targets of many forms of victimization, not only criminal assault.

What is an assailant looking for in a victim? Most, if not all of the time, someone who appears to be an easy prey. The assailant may be just as fearful as his intended victims are while he is determining who he is going to victimize or while committing the crime, so it is all the more important that he pick someone who won't resist when confronted. Any sign of confidence by the intended victim may be all it takes to make the assailant abandon the plan or select another victim.

Going back to basic principles of nature and the predator/prey concept of survival of the fittest, natural evolution dictates that a species will become extinct unless it evolves and develops alternative measures to protect itself from its predator. As law-abiding citizens, we must take extra measures to survive attacks by criminal predators out to render us extinct, so to speak.

THE FUD FACTORS

Criminals use the "FUD" factors to complete most, if not all, personal crimes. They rely on **fear, uncertainty and doubt**. They know most people become extremely fearful when confronted, are uncertain about what to do and doubt their ability to do anything but obey the assailant's demands.

The FUD factors can be just as effective when used against the assailant. Everything you employ to decrease your chances of becoming a crime victim involve elements of the FUD factors. Make the assailant wonder if you are a good choice as a victim.

LOOK AND ACT CONFIDENT

You have only one opportunity to make a first impression, and when it can make the difference between being hurt or slain and escaping from your assailant, it is of the utmost importance that you make a "good" first impression. It is critical that you are confident in your plan, no matter how threatening the circumstances.

The only way to develop confidence is through knowledge — of what an assailant looks for in a victim and of what puts fear, uncertainty and doubt in the mind of the assailant. Knowledge of techniques or ploys that you are confident of will give you the security to put the plan into action. The more ways you learn to outsmart an assailant, the more confident you will become.

MAKE EYE CONTACT AND SPEAK

If there is one habit we seemed to have abandoned as a society, it is the practice of making eye contact and speaking to people we pass while walking. We decided as a society that it was dangerous to look at other people and speak.

Eye contact with another person is usually avoided because we are either inattentive or insecure. Both of those traits must be overcome. Perhaps because of the way we were raised, we may feel it is rude to make eye contact or believe doing so invites a confrontation. Being attentive to your surroundings, knowing what to do and having a plan of action allow you to be more secure in yourself.

The way you speak sends a message to the person you are meeting. As I point out in my seminars, there are two very distinct ways to say hello. One way is strictly businesslike and usually includes a nod of the head and little, if any, smile. The other is commonly referred to as the "friendly hello," which is sometimes misinterpreted as flirting.

You can develop the habit of speaking to strangers and sending the message you want them to receive. Practice by experimenting with different ways of saying "hello" to yourself in a mirror. Then practice on everyone you meet.

By making eye contact early in an encounter and speaking as you approach, you accomplish several important objectives.

Show the Person You Are Not Afraid

That is the first step in developing self-confidence. We all know people who aren't any more intelligent or any more dedicated as employees than we are, but they always seem to get their way. How are they different?

Ninety-five percent of the time, the only difference is they have an assertive personality. They have a persistence that wears other people down. Most people are nonassertive by choice which makes it easier for the few who are assertive. This is not to insinuate that you should become obnoxious and bullish in your personality, but you must become strong in your convictions (morality). That development of assertiveness and confidence is important in avoiding becoming the victim of an assailant.

You Control the Contact

When you make eye contact and speak, you control the contact, which is critical while you are determining the person's motives. You will have taken the offensive in the contact and, rather than being intimidated and waiting to react, you might say you have become the aggressor.

You Know What They Look and Sound Like

When you make eye contact and speak, you send two important messages. You let the person know you obviously have some idea of what he looks like, and, if you speak and force him to respond, you can probably identify his voice.

If you planned to mug or rob someone, wouldn't you prefer to select victims who hadn't even looked at you as you approached them? What kind of signs would they be sending if they wouldn't even look at or speak to you? They either aren't paying attention to what is happening around them or they won't look because they are afraid.

That is the kind of victim most attackers look for. Why would they want to assault someone who could identify them physically and could possibly recognize their voice?

Predators seek the easiest prey. If an assailant passes two potential victims and one speaks and makes eye contact and the next doesn't look or speak, which is he going to choose? Don't make it easy for him to choose you.

Force the Person to Respond Before He Is Ready

By making eye contact and speaking, you are controlling the contact, even if he means you no harm. That will develop your assertiveness and confidence in personal relationships and can help you in other areas, such as your job.

In the situation you were faced with earlier in this chapter, where you were totally isolated with the person standing at your car, one of the first things you must do is to make eye contact and speak to him. If he is considering you as a victim, you have just communicated to him that you are not afraid to speak, and you force him to react.

Walk Erectly

How you look is often more important than what you say or how you say it. We all tend to stereotype people by their appearance, whether we realize it or not. Some people are intimidating simply because of their size. Others are intimidating because of their facial expressions. And others are intimidating simply by the way they walk. How you walk can determine your chances of being criminally victimized as much as any other characteristic.

We have all seen or known people who were large but not intimidating, just because of their posture. Likewise, we have all met people who weren't big or muscular, but conveyed the feeling that they weren't someone you would want angry at you. Often, we form our opinions about a person based on how they carry themselves. Assailants do the same.

Criminals confined in different prisons around the country for personal crimes (muggings, sexual assault, robbery, assault and battery) were shown videotapes of people walking down the street and were asked to pick those who they would target as victims. When the results were tabulated, the criminals picked essentially the same people.

Asked why they picked the particular people, they had no specific reason. Their response was the same as that of the criminal I referred to earlier: "They just looked like victims."

After studying the victims selected for some time, researchers could detect no one common characteristic. Some were large men, some were small women. Some not chosen were small and elderly or slightly built. It seemed unrelated to size, sex, age or race.

Finally, a computer analysis was conducted of those chosen and the only common characteristic was the way they walked. They walked like victims, with their heads down, possibly with a shuffle. They didn't walk with head erect or appear to be paying attention to where they were heading. They didn't walk heel to toe, which is a walk of confidence, an upright walk that indicates you know where you are going.

It appears that many people are chosen simply by the way they carry themselves.

In facing the person alone at your car, first make eye contact and speak. Do not slow down as you approach or stop and consider retreating. If anything, you must speed up as though you are some figure of authority wanting to question him about his presence near your car.

WHAT TO DO WHEN FOLLOWED

If you are being followed, the last thing you should do is speed up your pace. If you do, you have just told the assailant what he wanted to know: You are scared.

Have you ever watched a dog confront a cat? When a dog first confronts a cat, it acts with caution until determining whether the cat is afraid. The dog will run toward the cat to elicit a reaction. If the cat begins to run, the dog will immediately give chase. If the cat stops and prepares to defend itself, most dogs will run near the cat and stop, sniff around, or bark and usually abandon the plan.

Human aggressors are similar. They look for signs of weakness shown in the first few seconds of an encounter with a potential victim. If they sense fear or insecurity in the intended victim, they attack. If they sense security or "morality" in an intended victim, quite often they will abandon the plan.

For those of you who are doubting the application of the analogy, have patience. There are several other ploys you can combine with making eye contact, speaking and walking confidently. You won't rely only on those techniques, but they play an inherent role in lessening your chances of becoming a victim of assault.

When I discuss speaking to the individual, I'm not just talking about saying hello. There are certain things you can say in the initial conversation that will make the person wonder about you. You want the assailant wondering, "Why on earth is this person not afraid?" You want him to experience the FUD factors — fear, uncertainty and doubt — about your availability as a victim. You want him to think he may become the victim.

ROLE-PLAY

Have you ever had someone approach you and act as if he is a former acquaintance, and you had no idea who he was? Talk about uncertainty and doubt: You not only wonder who he is, but you immediately start to question your own sanity. For that moment, did you forget what your plans were or stop what you were doing? Would you victimize someone who just walked up to you smiling as though you are some long-lost cousin?

You can create uncertainty and doubt in any stranger by saying something like, "Hey, how have you been doing, I haven't seen you in quite some time!" Or point at them and say, "Don't I know you?"

Whether or not the person intends to do you harm, you have totally confused him. If he did intend to harm you, he now has to deal with an unexpected turn of events. You think you know him. What could be worse for an assailant?

To complete your turning of the tables, continue the conversation with, "You don't remember me, do you? I'm Jane Doe, I was your federal parole officer after you got out of the joint! You're Michael L. Norman, aren't you?" With that, you have just put the "fear" in FUD to work! If there is one person a criminal wants to avoid, it is anyone associated with law enforcement.

Put yourself in the assailant's place for just a moment and think what would be flashing through your mind. You would no longer be thinking about how much money the other person is carrying. You might be thinking here is someone who (1) isn't afraid to approach me and speak, (2) thinks he knows me or someone who looks enough like me to make him think he knows me, (3) can identify me later, (4) even worse, is some type of law enforcement official, the last person in the world I want to visit with about the past or future, and (5) is a federal parole officer, which means he is probably armed, and the penalty for assaulting even a federal janitor is probably at least a gazillion years!

You have just incorporated "active role-play," the second method of not looking like a victim, into your arsenal of DEFENSIVE LIVING skills. In a manner of speaking, the assailant has now become the prey.

ACTIVE ROLE-PLAY

I travel often in my job as a marketing manager. On one trip, I stopped at a shopping center in a small town in southern Arkansas to use a pay phone to check for messages at my office. I was walking back to my car when a man pulled up, jumped out of his car and started cursing at me and screaming as he approached, "I'm going to kill you if you try to repossess my furniture!" You can imagine the confusion I experienced at that moment.

I then realized that the pay phone was adjacent to the front door of a rent-to-own furniture and appliance store. It seems that someone had just called from the store and told the man that someone was on the way to repossess his furniture. Guess who he thought I was? Talk about being in the wrong place at the wrong time.

Immediately, I noticed a drive-in bank in the middle of the shopping center and said, "Mister, I don't have any idea what you are talking about. We got a tip that this bank is going to be robbed and if you blow my cover, I'm going to be very upset! Now get out of here!"

It was amazing how quickly his attitude changed. Suddenly, this crazed maniac was apologizing as he quickly walked back to his car. He then left the area and as far as I know, or care, didn't come back.

The incident occurred during the time I was writing this book. I couldn't help but smile after it was over, but at the moment it was happening, it wasn't funny.

MAKE YOUR ASSAILANT THE VICTIM

A most effective way to not look like a victim is to make the assailant think *he* is the victim. Your ultimate goal is to avoid a physical confrontation. Outsmarting a potential assailant through the use of role-play is another way of defeating him intelligently, not physically.

I have been teaching role-play techniques to law enforcement officers for years. Such methods take some practice but are extremely effective in defeating an opponent without fighting, even for the average person.

In most of the roles I will discuss in this book, I avoid impersonating an officer and instead use the power of suggestion to make the potential assailant think I am some kind of authority.

In the situation I described earlier, in which you are approaching your car and are isolated when suddenly someone appears near your car, to turn and run at that point is out of the question. You must take the initiative by making eye contact, looking confident as though *you* are the predator, and go into a role.

If the stranger is a white male, your first comment could be something like, "Hey! Have you seen a black guy around here the last few minutes? We just had an armed robbery, and we are looking for a black male about your height."

If the person standing near your car is a black male, then you would say, "Hey! Have you seen a white guy around here in the last few minutes? We just had an armed robbery, and we are looking for a white male about your height." Make sure you don't describe the person with whom you are role-playing.

If he was thinking about assaulting you, what would he be thinking after hearing that? First, are you some kind of authority, the last person he wants to assault or help? Second, you said "we" are looking for a criminal, so it sounds as though more troops are on the way or nearby. And third, if you are looking for an armed robber, you definitely aren't afraid of him and you're probably armed.

As you continue to your car, add, if needed, "Keep your hands where I can see them," never taking your eyes off the person. You then brush by him quickly, get in your car and "go chase the bad guys."

What you have accomplished is the defeat of the assailant with your intelligence. And in this particular role-play, you did not impersonate a police officer. You led the person to make some erroneous assumptions.

CAN'T BEAT 'EM? JOIN 'EM!

An attractive woman who worked in a shoe store was being harassed by a man who frequented her store almost daily. He began to make verbal sexual advances and over a period of weeks became increasingly agitated when she kept refusing to even wait on him. When he began to follow her around town, she literally feared for her safety.

She attended one of my DEFENSIVE LIVING seminars and told me of the problem. Realizing that she indeed had the right to be left alone, she decided that two could play the game. She decided to fight the battle intelligently, and we prepared a role-play.

The next time he came in the store, she played the role to perfection.

She immediately approached the man, apologized for her behavior the last few weeks and then proceeded to justify her behavior. Once she explained that she really didn't know the first thing about shoes and that she was only working there as a cover to investigate a large narcotics ring, it was amazing how apologetic he became.

She further explained that members of her "team" had observed his extreme interest in her and were becoming increasingly concerned about his knowledge of their "operation." She advised him that for his own safety he should abandon any romantic thoughts he might have toward her, and she made him swear to secrecy about the operation. Also, for his own safety, he should perhaps do his shoe shopping at another store so he wouldn't become a suspect in the investigation.

After more than six months, she hasn't seen or heard from the man.

For those of you who might be thinking you could never be convincing in this form of "assault prevention," let me again remind you of the alternatives. Picture yourself in an elevator, or on an isolated parking deck, and the only other people around are a couple of rough-looking thugs. You have two choices: You can look like the prey and try to react if confronted, or you can look like the predator, with eye contact, verbal action and role-play if necessary. Which seems like the silly action to take?

If you still question the effectiveness of role-play, don't forget — criminals also frequently use the method to commit their crimes. One of the most popular and effective methods used by criminals in child abductions is to impersonate an officer. Make sure you discuss with your children, frequently, the "roles" criminals may use.

You are limited only by your own imagination and personality in developing a few scenarios you could have available in an emergency. It takes a little practice, but even that can be enjoyable.

FIGHT SMARTER, NOT HARDER

A participant in one of my seminars, a schoolteacher, shared one of her experiences since developing the art of role-play to increase her confidence.

She was on an elevator with several people when two young thugs got on and began to direct racial slurs at a man who was obviously new to the United States. He, along with everyone else on the elevator, became visibly apprehensive.

Without thinking, the woman said in an authoritative voice as she glared directly at one of the culprits, "Didn't I just arrest you about three months ago for shoplifting? Aren't you Robert Jackson?"

"No, Ma'am, not me, my name is John Wilson!" was his immediate reply.

"You sure could pass for his twin. You better hope he never gets charged with murder, because we will surely be picking you up for questioning!"

She said she could almost cut the tension in the air until she took control. The last minute of the ride to the lobby was quiet and uneventful as everyone stared at the two thugs, who remained silent and appeared anxious to leave the elevator.

Listening to her retell the story, I could sense her pride in herself. She said she was sure that had she not taken that action, some kind of assault would have occurred. She also said how surprised she was, since she didn't consider herself aggressive. She then reminded me of how I had ended the seminar she had attended. She was able to repeat my quote exactly.

"Those who excel at resolving difficulties do so before they arise, for to win one hundred victories in one hundred battles is not the acme of skill. To defeat the enemy without fighting is the true acme of skill."

Sun Tzu

ROLE-PLAY OF LAST RESORT

It is with reservation that I even mention this technique, but sometimes the law-abiding citizen seems to be the only one not protected by our laws. Very few, if any, police officers would arrest a person for using whatever means available to avoid being victimized by an assailant.

As a law enforcement trainer and a former police officer, I know firsthand the fear most criminals experience when confronted by any form of law enforcement authority. However, let me be very specific about the intent of this kind of role-play, impersonating a police officer: It is not intended to be used except when you are faced with the threat of serious bodily harm or death.

The only time you would impersonate a police officer is when it is the method of last resort. And if so, your intent is not to impersonate an officer but to "survive" what you consider to be a serious threat to your safety by "outsmarting" your assailant.

Even if you were to blatantly impersonate an officer, if you feel your life is in danger and it is a matter of impersonating an officer or becoming the victim of an assailant, the choice should be rather simple.

Many assailants pretend to be an officer to "arrest" a child or a victim for sexual assault. Do not attempt to arrest someone. You are only trying to save your life, so use the least amount of physical force necessary to prevent injury to any of the parties involved, especially yourself.

The intent is not criminal. It is only to survive. I feel sorry for an officer who would blame you for trying to avoid victimization using such means. Most officers would prove understanding once you had an opportunity to explain your actions.

PASSIVE ROLE-PLAY

For those who still don't think they have the personality or appearance to use such FUD techniques as active role-play, there are still other ways to not look like a victim. Of these, passive role-play is the most effective method of all.

As a police officer, while off duty, I arrested a person one evening as he attempted to break into a car on a shopping mall parking lot. I wish I could say I observed the attempted theft taking place, but I didn't. My car was parked several yards away and there were dozens of cars between mine and the one he was attempting to steal. As I walked to my car, someone yelled for the police and said someone was breaking into an automobile.

I quickly approached the young boy, identified myself as a police officer and told him he was under arrest. His first comment was, "I knew better! I'll bet your car is that gray Mustang over there, isn't it?" A little surprised, I said, "Yes, how did you know that?"

"Because I was going to steal it until I saw your handcuffs hanging on the turn signal. When I saw them, I started to go to another parking lot, but thought I could get out of here before anyone noticed, especially you."

Even though I am no longer a police officer, you can guess what is always in my car when I am away from it. The first thing you see when you look in my car is a pair of handcuffs hanging on the turn signal and a copy of *Law and Order* magazine on the passenger seat.

I keep the handcuffs and the magazine under the seat when driving, but always place them in clear view when I leave my car. Not only has it never been broken into, but the practice seems to be a great way to avoid parking tickets. So far.

The photograph at right is of my car. If two cars were parked side-by-side, and you as a thief had to make a quick decision on which car to burglarize or steal, which would you choose? The car with a police magazine in the seat and a pair of handcuffs hanging on the turn signal, or the car beside it with a box of tissue on the seat and an attache case lying on the back seat?

For most criminals, it would be an easy choice. Most likely, though, a criminal would abandon any plan to steal or burglarize either one, since it appears a police officer could be somewhere in the vicinity.

There are many innovative ways to not look like a victim. Not only for you but also your car, home and other property. Because you are in your home or car a great part of the time, by making them not look like a victim you lessen your chances of becoming a crime victim.

DON'T MAKE YOUR CAR
LOOK LIKE A VICTIM

Walk up to ten cars in a shopping mall parking lot and look at the inside of each one and you will be amazed at how much information is available about the owner of each car.

One car might have a Bible in the front seat and the next might have a pornographic magazine. One might have makeup and a hair brush and the next, shotgun shells on the floorboard. You shouldn't leave anything visible other than what you want seen in order to convey the desired message.

People often unknowingly tell a great deal about their personality and identity by what is on and in their car. You can often determine their sex, personality type and age by the decals or bumper stickers on their car.

Let's say you are a single female who frequently has to drive alone at night. Which bumper sticker might make a criminal think twice about you as a victim?

> THIS CAR STOPS AT ALL YARD SALES

That bumper sticker is self-explanatory. Do you think it would conjure up any fear, uncertainty or doubt in the mind of an assailant?

> THIS CAR PROTECTED BY SMITH AND WESSON

What about that one? Most criminals know that Smith and Wesson is the largest handgun manufacturer in the world. If you as an assailant were considering following this potential victim, what might go through your mind? There is an indirect message that this person may be armed, and even if she isn't, her husband, boyfriend or son is, even if *he* doesn't exist.

> I'M A PISTOL PACKIN' MAMA

By displaying a bumper sticker like the one above, you definitely plant seeds of uncertainty and doubt in the mind of a criminal about your willingness to be victimized.

I can assure you from firsthand experience that bumper stickers like the second and third ones and those of the National Rifle Association get attention. As a police officer, I always approached a vehicle with a bumper sticker like those much more cautiously than one with:

> Pardon My Driving, but I'm Putting on My Makeup

My neighbor's van was stolen from a church parking lot while she was attending services. She had left her purse on the passenger seat in full view. The thief broke into the van and drove it to an isolated part of town, where he destroyed the interior. He ripped out the cellular telephone and half the dash with it, cut all of the seats and broke all the windows out. The van was recovered the next day.

I asked the woman why she left her purse in the front seat. "I never thought anyone would break into my van on a church parking lot" was her reply.

Being the victim of a theft of property, such as your automobile, can be very traumatic. What seems like a minor property crime can create numerous other problems. Not only did she lose more than $200 and her purse, but she also suffered the inconvenience of having her van in a repair shop for several weeks, creating other hardships.

The mental stress associated with even a property crime can be overwhelming, especially when family heirlooms or keepsakes are taken.

There are many ways to not look like a victim. In this particular case, this woman was indirectly victimized by allowing her van to look like a victim.

POINTS ON YOUR VEHICLE'S APPEARANCE

1. A criminal shouldn't be able to tell whether the owner is male or female, but send masculine signals.
2. Don't have anything visible that will tempt a thief.
3. Put valuables in the trunk.
4. Borrow a business card from a police officer and place it on the dashboard.

OTHER PASSIVE WAYS TO
NOT LOOK LIKE A VICTIM

What you wear can also have a significant impact on your chances of being victimized. There are many subtle ways to make a possible assailant fearful, uncertain and doubtful about choosing you as a victim.

One of my former karate students is a Special Agent with the FBI and his wife is an avid runner. She always runs with other women, but on several occasions has been harassed and verbally intimidated by men passing by in vehicles. Almost daily, some man asks her if she needs a ride.

When I asked to see her running tops, it confirmed what I had suspected. They were all typical runner's tops: Thin and sleeveless, which I know are comfortable. However, the criminal who specializes in sexual assault would think the tops are suggestive.

I recommended that she wear one of her husband's T-shirts with the large "FBI" printed on the front and back and see if that didn't help. I also equipped one of her two running mates with a "Dallas Police Department" T-shirt and another with a "Federal Law Enforcement Training Center" T-shirt. At first, they thought the idea was silly. That was until they realized weeks later that their "fan club" had dwindled considerably and they hadn't been harassed at all. Wearing those imposing tops when running has greatly reduced the annoyance they once felt.

T-shirts, lapel pins, tie tacks and handcuffs can all be effective passive weapons. You can buy a pair of handcuffs for $15 to $20 at any police equipment supply store. The cuffs are not only an effective tool in avoiding criminals, but also in avoiding "spare change artists" on the street. By wearing them so they are partially exposed, as though you don't really want them seen, they can be effective. You wouldn't think something as small as a tie tack or lapel pin in the shape of a pair of handcuffs would be noticeable, but a criminal can spot them immediately. They, too, don't want to become a "victim."

DRESSED TO KILL

When vacationing, it is important to wear something other than souvenirs. Criminals prey on tourists, and the last thing you want to look like when vacationing is a tourist. Criminals know the chance of a victim from out of state spending the money to come back and testify is slim to none.

Don't walk down a street with souvenirs hanging from every limb of your body, dressed in bermuda shorts with black knee socks and dress shoes. To an assailant, you appear to be a victim longing to be assaulted. Especially when you finish off your ensemble with a pair of binoculars, or a camera around your neck, and exclaim to your wife every ten seconds, "Gosh Ethyl, look how tall that building is!"

If an assailant doesn't get you then, he will get you when you return to the hotel. You're the kind that is worth following.

If you and your family are walking in unfamiliar surroundings while on vacation, wouldn't you agree that your chances of being victimized are much less if you are wearing a "New York Police Department" T-shirt or windbreaker than if you are wearing a DisneyWorld "Mickey Mouse" T-shirt? Why would a criminal even take a chance? There are too many easy victims available.

It's comparable to putting a burglar alarm decal on the window of your car, even if you don't have an alarm system. If two cars are parked side-by-side and one has an alarm sticker and the other doesn't, which one is more likely to be broken into? It's worth spending a couple of dollars for some decals if it deters one incident of vandalism or theft.

Many of the "experts" who read this would say a professional thief won't be hindered in the least by a decal. I agree, the professional criminal is going to be more difficult to defeat, but the majority of criminals are not Rhodes scholars. If they were that good at committing crimes, our prisons wouldn't be overflowing.

All of my Ten Tips will enable you to lessen your chances of looking like a victim. But each of the nine remaining tips is an extension of **Tip 1, Don't Think and Look Like a Victim.**

2

Tip 2

Always Lock the Doors In Your Car and Home Immediately After Entering or Exiting

---

The young executive said goodbye to his friends after dinner, put on his coat and left the club. Outside the door, a uniformed policeman, hired by the club to work security, was walking a woman to her car. The executive headed to his car, hopped in, started the engine and headed home.

As he sat at the parking lot exit, waiting for a break in the line of traffic, his door was suddenly opened and a stranger shoved a gun in his face and demanded his money. He quickly looked for the policeman as he reached for his wallet. The policeman was about fifty feet away, but was walking the other way, escorting the woman to her car.

It took only seconds for him to relinquish his wallet and for the thief to disappear into the night. As he continued to sit in his car and gather his nerves, he thought to himself, "If I had only locked my doors!"

YOUR CAR: A BARRIER OR A TRAP?

Your car or home can be an effective barrier against assault and abduction if used correctly, or they can become a deadly trap if used incorrectly.

When you exit your car, do you lock your doors?

When I conduct my Ten Tips seminars, I ask the audience this question. Most everyone raises their hands to indicate they do.

Can you honestly say that right now the doors to your automobile are locked?

Quite often, fifty percent to seventy-five percent of the audience responds that their doors are locked.

Do you lock your car door immediately after entering your vehicle?

Only ten percent to fifteen percent of most audiences claim that they do lock their car doors after entering their vehicle.

What would you do if, as you were getting into your vehicle, someone walked up and pointed a gun at you and said, "Get in the car, move over to the passenger side, or I'll kill you?"

THREE OPTIONS

Would you get in the car as ordered?

Usually about sixty percent to seventy-five percent of the audience raise their hands to denote they would obey the assailant's command.

Would you not get in the car?

Normally, only five percent to ten percent of the audience say they would not comply.

Or do you not have any idea what you would do?

That question gets a "yes" from twenty-five percent to fifty percent of the audience. Usually several who responded to the first two choices now reconsider and choose the third option. The third option is always accompanied by laughter from the audience, because most people have no idea what they would or should do. Almost everyone assumes that something as violent as an abduction could never happen to them or someone they know. However, by the end of the seminar, very few if any will ever find the thought amusing again.

If it happens, you may have **one to five seconds** to decide what you will do.

ALWAYS LOCK THE DOORS TO YOUR CAR IMMEDIATELY AFTER ENTERING

It is amazing to me how many people still do not lock their doors once they get in their vehicle. This is one of the simplest and most effective forms of assault prevention to practice. If you don't believe it, read your local newspaper and within a week, you will most likely read of someone being assaulted simply because he did not have his automobile doors locked. If used correctly, your vehicle can help you escape an assailant's attempt to victimize you.

APPROACHING YOUR VEHICLE

Have your key in your hand (preferably your left) and be ready to immediately unlock your door when you arrive at your vehicle.

How many times have you arrived at your car door or the door of your home and, realizing you couldn't find your keys, started fumbling around in your purse or pockets trying to find them? **Tip 1, Don't Think and Look Like a Victim.**

You must be ready to unlock your vehicle and get on your way as quickly and smoothly as possible. The best way to accomplish that is to have your keys out and ready before leaving your last safe area.

That car or house key can become effective as a striking or jabbing weapon in an emergency. In Tip 6, which deals with the advantages and disadvantages of weapons for self-protection, I will explain how a key can be one of the most effective such weapons.

As you approach your vehicle, observe as much of the perimeter of the area as possible.

Always approach your vehicle from the driver's side. That angle enables you to observe the front, rear and driver's side. It leaves only the passenger side as a possible hiding place for an assailant, and that side can be observed by looking underneath the car as you approach from a distance.

If your doors are locked as they should be, the assailant has to somehow get around to the driver's side without being observed.

ENTERING YOUR VEHICLE

If someone plans to abduct or assault you, your vehicle quite often becomes his assistant in committing the crime. He will attempt to take you from the public's view in your vehicle. The assailant can't afford to expose his plan too soon, or you won't be close enough to your vehicle for it to be used in the assault. However, the criminal can't wait too long, because you just might lock your door after entering.

One of the most critical times for assault and abduction prevention occurs in the one to five seconds you are unlocking and entering your vehicle. That "window" of time is critical.

You should be especially concerned with assaults originating from the rear of the vehicle. In ninety percent to ninety-five percent of abductions using the victim's vehicle, the attacker approaches his victim from the rear.

I cannot overemphasize the importance of the proper approach to and entry of your vehicle. The way most people enter a vehicle sets them up to be victimized.

As you unlock the car door, use your left hand to unlock the door and face the rear of the vehicle.

That method serves three important functions. It permits you to observe the rear of the vehicle, which is the most common hiding place for an attacker. It enables you to stand sideways, which makes it much more difficult for you to be forced into the vehicle, and virtually eliminates the chance of being forced into the car without at least seeing the assailant. And it leaves your right hand

free to ward off an attack, either by using a deterrent, such as a pepper spray weapon, or by pushing the assailant away with your free hand long enough for you to regain your composure. You also have the car key in the left hand to use as a weapon.

Most people unlock the door with their right hand and face the car, thus leaving themselves vulnerable. That makes it easy for an assailant to push them into their car.

After you have opened the door, if you are facing toward the driver's seat, the area becomes a trap; it limits your path of escape. The driver's door actually aids the assailant because it serves as a funnel to guide you into the car if pushed from behind. Even if you are not pushed completely into the car, the opened door serves as a barricade to prevent your escape.

Using proper approach and entry principles can often prevent an attack, because the element of surprise is reduced dramatically. In Tip 5, you will see that surprise is a key factor for assailants and victims alike. Quite often, an assailant will abandon a plan if the victim appears to be cautious and alert to his environment. Remember **Tip 1, Don't Look Like a Victim.**

Sometimes, because of circumstances on your part, such as parking in a well-lighted area or the lack of adequate cover, the attacker doesn't always hide behind the vehicle. Often he will time his approach to coincide with yours so that he arrives just as you are unlocking your door. And he might use one of many lures to distract you. One such stalling tactic is: "Excuse me, but could you tell me the time?" or, "Hey, did you know you have a flat tire over here?"

USING YOUR CAR AS A BARRIER TO ASSAULT

Among the best ways to use a car as a barrier against an abduction attempt if the attacker is attempting to force you into the car is to drop to the ground and crawl under the vehicle. Once under your car, begin screaming for help and use whatever self-protection device you have available. That also gives you time to find a weapon in case it is in your purse or pocket, the last place a weapon should be.

Crawling under your car can be an effective method of assault prevention for several reasons.

It will now be practically impossible for an assailant to abduct or assault you. Have you ever tried to get a dog or cat from under a car? Can you imagine trying to get a child from under a car, much less an adult? Especially when you are kicking and slapping at the assailant and screaming the entire time! Realistically, how long is that person going to continue the attack? Within a few seconds, it is going to become obvious that you are one difficult victim to deal with.

You surely aren't going to be sexually assaulted while under your car. Unless the assailant has a weapon, there is very little he can do to you while you are under your car. You are going to be screaming for assistance the entire time, and if you are near other people, the assailant is not going to stay around and be identified by anyone coming to your aid.

The worst an unarmed assailant — and many assailants are unarmed — is going to be able to do is curse you and perhaps throw something at you, just as some people do when their cat or dog gets under a car.

Be sure you have your keys with you in case the assailant tries to steal your car. Under the car is obviously not the place to be if you left your keys in it.

A question I am always asked at seminars when I offer this method of assault prevention is, "What if I can't fit under my car?" It is amazing what you can do while trying to save your life.

Take a deep breath and wedge yourself under the car. The assailant will never get you out then.

YOUR CAR AS A BARRIER WHEN YOU ARE NOT IN IT

A young woman who had attended one of my seminars was recently the subject of an attempted abduction.

As she arrived at her home, she didn't notice the unfamiliar car near her driveway until after she had parked. She did, however, use **Tip 4, Take 15 to 30 Seconds to Observe Your Surroundings**, before getting out of her locked vehicle. Noticing the car and not recognizing it, she thought nothing else of it since she didn't see anyone inside.

As she got out of her car and locked it, a man rose up in the parked car, got out quickly, and approached her from the rear of her car. She saw him in time to move to the front of her car. As he approached the side of the car, he demanded that she come to him, telling her he had a gun. She immediately moved to the other side of the car rather than obey his order and told him he would have to shoot her before she would surrender. That's an example of morality, or believing in a cause!

He obviously was bluffing about the weapon, since he never produced it or even mentioned it again. After several moves of chase, such as we have seen children play around a car, he realized he couldn't get to her without running around the car. As he moved to make another attempt, she bolted to a nearby neighbor's house, screaming the entire way, not knowing if the assailant was behind her. He immediately fled to his vehicle and escaped.

This story had a happy ending. Many don't. The young woman was able to use her car as a barrier to keep the attacker at a safe distance until she could get her thoughts together. She realized that fleeing to a neighbor's home where lights were on would probably make the assailant think twice about pursuing.

USE YOUR CAR TO ESCAPE, NOT CONFRONT, AN ASSAILANT

Many seminar participants inquire about their legal responsibility if confronted by an assailant, or group of assailants, who attempt to block or stop their car. Many self-defense books and police departments tell people that if they think their life is in danger, they have the right to run over whoever is blocking their escape path.

A word of caution is in order regarding such a situation. It is always best to retreat when possible. Not only from a survival viewpoint, but also from a liability viewpoint. It is always best to back up and change your direction and escape. Don't make matters worse.

We might say we would just run someone down if confronted by a gang in the middle of a street. And more than likely you would be within your rights, if the situation were life-threatening. But it is difficult to know all the circumstances when a crowd is standing in the path of your vehicle late at night as you turn a corner.

There could have been a pedestrian hit by a car, drawing a crowd, or a fire in an apartment forcing people into the street. Or even worse, a police operation stopping all cars.

The laws on the use of force are no different when you are in a car and it becomes a weapon out of necessity. A citizen or police officer should always use the least amount of force necessary to escape bodily harm.

I will expand on the use of force in Tip 6, but for now, when possible, retreat, not confront! You can be held liable for any injuries you inflict if the force used was excessive for the situation. People are sued every day for "defending" themselves. A car is an excellent weapon in an emergency, but use it to escape, not attack, your assailant unless there in no path of retreat.

TURNING THE CAR INTO A TRAP FOR THE ASSAILANT

Many times I am asked what action should be taken if you are in a situation in which you feel you have no choice but to get in the car with the attacker. This could happen if you had just placed your child in the back seat and were then approached by an assailant demanding that you get in the car. Obviously you can't run away and leave your child alone with a criminal. Crawling under the car is still an option, as long as you have the keys with you.

Most women in my seminars say they would much rather get in the car with the assailant if their child is already inside. I can understand their innate drive to protect their young, but getting in the car with an assailant is not going to help you or your child. If necessary, throw your keys as far as you can and take your chances on surviving where you are. If it is night, the assailant will never find the keys, so what does he do then?

For those who feel they would have to obey the assailant's demands and get in the car if their child is already strapped in a child seat, there is still hope for you. As soon as you enter the car, immediately slide to the passenger side with your back against the passenger side door. As the assailant enters the driver's side, you should pull your knees up toward your chest and start what I refer to as a "bicycle" kick, pumping away at the assailant's upper body and head as fast as possible.

If the assailant has not closed the door before you start to kick, he will never get it closed. If he has already entered the driver's side and closed the door, I can assure you that he will not be able to open the door and escape fast enough.

Practicing this with students at seminars, we use a six-inch-thick pad between the victim and assailant, and it is still a painful kick to receive. Not only does this have a physical effect on the attacker, but it also makes him feel trapped with a wild person, and that is not what he expected.

What you have done is turn your car into a trap for the criminal. In teaching my "Active Resistance" seminars, I have found that even smaller men and women have excellent success with that technique, even across the width of a van.

Many people are abducted after entering and locking their vehicle, then being confronted by someone outside the car who is threatening them with a weapon. Whatever you do, don't allow an attacker to negotiate an entry into your "safe area" if you plan to remain in the car. I will detail several options you have in Tip 9.

OTHER WAYS TO USE YOUR CAR AS A BARRIER TO ASSAULT

Don't pull up close behind other cars at traffic signals or in congested traffic. Always leave plenty of room between your car and the car in front of you in case you have to suddenly change direction.

Many criminals work in teams and, especially at night, have been known to stop at a traffic signal in front of a victim's car, with their accomplice then bumping the victim's car from behind. The assailants then attack by breaking the window out and robbing and assaulting the victim. That is a common method used on victims who have out-of-state license plates.

For such situations, it probably doesn't seem so silly after all to have a "Fraternal Order of Police" decal in the back window or a "This Vehicle Protected by Smith and Wesson" bumper sticker. I can assure you that most criminals will pick another victim.

YOUR HOME AS A BARRIER TO ASSAULT

Even though everything I have discussed so far has been concerned with the automobile, the same principles apply to your home.

ALWAYS KEEP THE DOORS AND WINDOWS OF YOUR HOME LOCKED

I wish I could assume that everyone knows to always keep their home's doors and windows locked, but it is obvious to me, from reading daily crime reports in the newspapers, that this tip needs to be emphasized.

In one instance, in a Florida college town, all four murders on a particular campus were committed by an assailant entering the victim's apartment through an unlocked door or window. I wonder how many other windows or doors the killer unsuccessfully tried to enter before finding each of these four unlocked?

Your home can be an excellent barrier to victimization, but only if you use it intelligently. Do not make it easy for an attacker to enter your home. Many books are available that address ways to make your home physically much more secure. What I want to ensure, though, is that you are aware of how to avoid mental mistakes that would make your home a trap, rather than a barrier against assault.

When you are in your home and the assailant is on the outside, then your home serves as a barrier to assault. But when you and the assailant are in your home at the same time, then your home becomes a trap!

YOUR HOME AS A TRAP

The salesman was a neatly dressed college-age man who said he was trying to pay his way through college by selling children's books during the summer break. My wife explained to the young man that she was not interested, but his sales training enabled him to gain a few more seconds by overcoming every objection my wife countered with.

Without my wife realizing it, he gradually worked his way in the front door as they talked and then seated himself on the sofa, uninvited. Continuing to espouse all the benefits of the books and overcoming her remaining objections, as many "hard sell" salespeople do, he had just about convinced her to purchase the books.

As she began to write the check for a down payment, it fortunately dawned on her that she was about to become another victim of this con artist. She abruptly stopped writing the check, tore it up and advised him she would rather talk with her husband before making a financial commitment.

Suddenly, this nicely dressed, well-mannered young man turned into a raging, foul-mouthed "crazy" person, as my wife described him later. She recalled, "I thought he was going to attack me at any second."

At that point, realizing she had committed a major error in admitting him into the house, she fortunately still had the knowledge to outsmart her possible assailant. Thinking quickly, she apologized to the young man for upsetting him and informed him that she had decided to go ahead and purchase the books without consulting me. She told him she would rather pay with cash, and that way no one would even know she had purchased them.

Suddenly, he reverted to the well-mannered young man she had met a few minutes earlier. As she excused herself, he remained seated on the sofa and reassured her what an intelligent decision she had made in deciding to buy the books.

He had no idea how intelligent her decision really was, because rather than retrieve her purse, she casually walked out the back door and went immediately to a neighbor's home and called the police.

By the time the police arrived, he had escaped in his car. I'm sure that once he realized he was the only one in the house, his heartbeat was close to what my wife's had been a few minutes earlier. The frightening part of the story is that no one else in the neighborhood had been called on by the salesman that day.

Who knows what would have happened to my wife had she not acted intelligently? And how many others has he victimized financially or physically? We both often wonder whom he is calling on today.

NEVER LET A STRANGER INTO YOUR HOME

If an assailant is in your home with you, the house becomes a trap, rather than a barrier. You are isolated from any assistance, thus giving the assailant a much greater chance of completing his crime undiscovered. Once you admit a total stranger into your home and close the door, you can be at risk. For your own sake, if you do admit strangers into your home, be a good judge of character.

Many people are victimized every day in their homes by criminals posing as salespeople, painters, missionaries and anything else they think will work to get in. One of the most common methods still favored by criminals to gain entry into a victim's home is to ask to borrow the phone to make an emergency call.

EMERGENCY CALLS

Every day, someone is victimized by an assailant posing as a motorist in distress or lost and needing to make a phone call. Make sure everyone in your family follows the same procedures when someone asks to use the telephone.

If someone comes to your home asking to make a phone call, never let that person come inside. You have several safe alternatives that can prevent you or a family member from turning your home from a barrier to a trap.

Offer to place the call for the person as he remains outside. Explain that you were once the victim of an assailant who used that method to gain entry into your home. If the person is in genuine need of assistance, he will be appreciative of your help, not offended. If he intends to do you harm, then you have already communicated that you don't plan to become a victim. That is by far the safest procedure to follow if you intend to lend assistance.

If you have a cordless phone, offer to let the person use it outside your home, and be careful to close your door behind you if you do step outside with him.

If you do allow someone in your home, don't let the house become a trap. Remain outside or near the door and never follow the person into the interior of your home. I know this may seem a bit extreme, but you must not let yourself or your child, if home alone, become isolated with a possible assailant in your home. If you are going to allow a complete stranger in your home, whether it is a person in genuine distress or a criminal looking for a victim, either one will feel uncomfortable at being the only person in the house.

Ask other family members what they would do if someone came to the door requesting to use the phone. Entire families have been found slain after letting a "stranded motorist" inside their home to make a phone call.

Many of these crimes are never solved, because the criminal is not a local person, but instead travels from state to state until captured. You can read almost weekly of some serial killer who has killed his victims as he traveled aimlessly from state to state. While writing this chapter, I read of a twenty-eight-year-old commercial truck driver who has been charged with the murders of two women and is a prime suspect in the deaths of at least twenty-six other women killed along a route he has traveled for the last several years.

If confronted by a stranger at your door trying to sell something, make it clear you are not interested in whatever is being offered. Tell them your spouse sells the product part time when not working undercover as a police detective. That is usually enough to stop most sales pitches, and criminals, immediately.

If they continue to press to come in and begin to ease their way in the door, step out of the house. Move several feet outside the door so that they begin to feel uncomfortable being the only one in your house. If they are a legitimate salesperson and mean only "monetary" harm, your action will force them, in most instances, to come outside with you. If they still do not come out, then just turn around and walk to a neighbor's, leaving them standing in your home.

Most of the time, just stepping outside your door will generate the desired result of drawing them out as well. You can then make your "close" as you tell them you are not interested in their product while walking alone back into your home.

If an assailant tries to force you back into your home, you must not go; drop to the ground, crawl through or around the assailant and somehow get out of the house. Your life may depend on your ability to get out of your home before the assailant can close the door with the two of you inside.

HAVE AN ESCAPE PLAN

A woman who had just attended one of my seminars called recently to share the details of her near-victimization.

The fifty-year-old woman, who lived alone, was awakened by a noise at two o'clock in the morning. Opening her eyes, she observed the silhouette of a man climbing into her bedroom window. Remembering from the seminar that your home can become a trap, she immediately jumped from the bed and ran out the front door, screaming the entire way to her neighbor's house. The intruder also escaped, and went the opposite direction. She asked me if she had done the correct thing and I assured her she had. Since the intruder had not yet entered the home, she still had time to escape.

Had the intruder already been in her bedroom, escaping might not have been possible. Under those circumstances, it is usually best to do nothing and pretend to be asleep.

The next morning, it was discovered that the intruder had cut her phone line and turned off the main electrical breaker. He obviously knew the home was occupied or he wouldn't have cut the phone line, so she escaped a dangerous situation. Even though she was not assaulted, she was and still is very much a "victim."

As I pointed out in the introduction of this book, quite often the assault may last only seconds and cause no physical injuries. But the trauma remains for many years. From talking with the woman only briefly, I am certain her life has been changed dramatically by the incident.

Forget trying to get to a gun or using the phone. If you have enough time for either of those, you still have enough time to escape. If there is no alternate escape path, then your ability to survive depends greatly on how well you have planned a course of action for such an event. Most people have never thought about what they would do, and therefore usually do nothing. Fortunately for the woman who awakened to see an intruder crawling in her window, she had devised an escape plan after attending my seminar. She is probably the exception, rather than the rule.

You should have a fire escape plan, a severe weather plan and an assailant escape plan for your and your family's safety.

What should you do if you are awakened at two in the morning by the sound of breaking glass from a window or door?

If the sound is coming from another area of the house, you must exit through the nearest window or door. If you keep your bedroom door locked, don't go to see what is happening. Leave the house immediately by crawling out a bedroom window.

If you have a phone by your bed, as you always should, press 911, explain briefly what is happening, throw the phone down and get out of the house. Most "experts" say to stay on the phone with the authorities so that you can relay important information. Only if you can't escape your house in the opposite direction of the intruder should you stay in the house and on the phone. Emergency personnel will respond to a 911 call if there is no one on the line, so if you can escape, leave it off the hook and get out as quickly as possible.

Once outside, make as much noise and scream as loudly as you can as you run to a neighbor's for assistance. You want all the attention you can get and you want the intruder to know, or at least think, that help is on the way.

If you have children in the house, your escape plan will be the same. You must get assistance and let the intruder know you are going for help, hence the screaming as you flee. Few intruders, if any, are going to remain in your home once you have escaped and gone for assistance. They are not going to take the time to look for possessions, much less try to find anyone else in the house. You will ensure your children's safety much more by fleeing for assistance than attempting to locate the intruder and confront him.

Make sure everyone in the family knows their escape routes. If your child is ever faced with a fire or assailant, make sure he has a plan of escape and a preplanned source of assistance. Many assault and murder victims have been found huddled in an upstairs closet after attempting to hide from their assailant. You will see in Tip 5 that you must get as much distance between you and an assailant as quickly as possible.

SUMMARY

The most important point to remember from **Tip 2, Always Lock the Doors In Your Car and Home Immediately After Entering or Exiting**, is that your car or home can be a barrier or trap in an assault, depending on how you use them. If you are inside your car or home, they are a barrier to victimization only if you keep the assailant on the outside. Once the assailant is in either your car or home with you, they quickly become a trap. Never become isolated with an assailant in your home or automobile.

3

Tip 3

Always Use the Buddy System

Animals Animals © 1992 A.& M. SHAH

A thirty-five-year-old mother of three went shopping on her lunch hour with her best friend in an upscale department store.   After browsing the sale racks in the women's clothing dept, she told her friend she was going to the children's department to check on some items and would return in just a few minutes.   She had been there only a short time when she was approached by a well-dressed man who identified himself as the store security manager.   He then exhibited a security badge and requested that she accompany him to the manager's office for a few moments.

He told her that another security employee had seen her placing some clothing in her undergarments and that she would have to be searched by a female employee before being allowed to leave the store. Although upset at the accusation, she agreed to go with the security manager, knowing she was innocent of any crime.

Fortunately, as she was being escorted to the back of the store and through the stockroom doors, her friend observed her being led away. The friend attempted to catch up with her and find out what had taken place.   After searching fruitlessly for a few moments, she became increasingly concerned and asked that a sales clerk page the store manager.   The clerk informed her that the manager was at lunch.

She then asked to see the security manager, and was told that he too was at lunch. She explained to the clerk what had happened and her concern for her friend. Not being easily intimidated, she demanded that the clerk accompany her to the stockroom — because she was going there, "Employees Only" sign or not, to look for her friend. The clerk told all of the stockroom and office personnel what had happened, and a search began.

Within a few minutes, two employees came upon the "security manager," who had bound and gagged his victim and was undressing her in a secluded area of the stockroom. When confronted, he fled the store through a nearby exit and was never captured. Obviously, this assailant had planned his crime thoroughly, since he knew exactly when both the store and security managers would be at lunch. His only mistake was in assuming he had picked a "lone" victim.

Little did he know that, fortunately for the victim, she was not alone. Had she gone shopping alone that day, she would have surely become the victim of that sexual assailant. The victim, although in shock, was unharmed because of the quick response of her buddy and the employees of the store. Only because she was using the buddy system and had a friend who was determined to find out what had happened to her was she spared the grief of becoming another victim of criminal assault.

ALWAYS USE THE BUDDY SYSTEM

That is one of the easiest of my Ten Tips to follow and one that can provide immediate results with no training. Always go with a friend or group of friends when shopping or traveling. You see this tip included in most crime prevention programs, but the importance of it is not emphasized as it should be.

- The majority of violent crime victims are alone when assaulted and are victimized by a lone, unarmed assailant.